# IMPROVE YOUR

# COMPETITIVE

# STRATEGY

## A Guide for the

## Healthcare Executive

# IMPROVE YOUR COMPETITIVE STRATEGY

## A Guide for the Healthcare Executive

## Alan M. Zuckerman, FACHE

Health Administration Press

ACHE Management Series

**Library of Congress Cataloging-in-Publication Data**

Zuckerman, Alan M.
    Improve your competitive strategy  :  a guide for the healthcare executive  /
by Alan M. Zuckerman.
        p. cm.
    Includes bibliographical references and index.
    ISBN 1- 56793-177-4 (alk. paper)
    1.  Health service administrators.    2.  Health services administration.
    I.  Title.
RA971.3 .Z835 2002
362.1'068—dc21

                                                                2002017222

Acquisitions Editor: Audrey Kaufman; Project manager: Joyce Sherman; Text design: Matt Avery; Cover design: Greg Moore

Health Administration Press
A division of the Foundation of the American College of Healthcare Executives
1 North Franklin Street, Suite 1700
Chicago, IL 60606-3491
(312) 424-2800

# Table of Contents

# Preface

AS I REFLECT on the content of this book, I am amazed by the changes that have occurred in healthcare during my career over the past 30 years. At the outset of my career, and even during a large part of it, a book on competitive strategy in healthcare would have been outlandish. For much of that time, demand for healthcare services was booming and supply was unable to keep up with demand. Providers struggled to add capacity and meet the needs of the communities they served. Competition, such as it existed, was polite, and collaboration was just as common. But, more typically, the average healthcare organization was inwardly focused, neither a fierce competitor nor avid collaborator.

In most markets, this situation began to change in the late 1980s as the effects of full implementation of the inpatient prospective payment system took hold. Decreasing inpatient length of stay as a result of this payment system created excess inpatient capacity in many organizations for the first time in decades. The new phenomenon of excess capacity led to some competition among healthcare organizations. But because most were prospering financially and competition was new, little serious or sophisticated competition occurred.

By the mid-1990s, another wave of major reimbursement change was taking hold. Managed care led to greater excess capacity and ushered in an era of significant financial problems for many healthcare organizations. Federal cutbacks followed in the late 1990s, generating greater financial difficulties for nearly all healthcare organizations. While the primary response to these changes has been one of cutbacks, consolidations, mergers, and the like, these developments have given rise to a new level of interest in competition as a means to cope with the new environment. With demand growing modestly, if at all, in most markets and financial pressures commonplace, competition for market share is growing. The incremental revenues resulting from successful competitive thrusts, often in higher margin areas, can make the difference between surviving and thriving for healthcare organizations today.

Yet, even as the need for successful competitive strategies in healthcare has grown, the nature of competition has remained fairly basic, especially when contrasted with industries in which for-profit firms dominate. In preparing this book, I was struck by the differences in the level of sophistication of the healthcare literature versus the general business literature on this subject despite the fact that healthcare organizations have been operating in an increasingly competitive environment for nearly 15 years. My hope is that this book can make an important contribution to the competitive capabilities of healthcare executives and the organizations they manage.

This book contains three parts. Chapter 1 is a review of the general literature on competitive strategies, both inside and outside of healthcare. Chapters 2 through 7 examine each of the main competitive strategy approaches used in healthcare. Each chapter is organized in a similar manner: the competitive strategy approach is defined and explained, and its applicability to healthcare organizations is examined; both business and healthcare literature pertaining to the particular approach is reviewed; and finally, case examples within and outside of healthcare are presented to illustrate the application of the competitive strategy. Chapters 8 through 10 constitute the third part of the book and attempt to provide a framework for carrying out more effective competitive strategy by healthcare organizations in the future. Chapter 8 addresses head-on the often-cited problem of data deficiencies and argues that data are plentiful, available, and not a limiting factor in applying competitive approaches. It also describes basic analytical techniques that are immediately applicable to healthcare organizations in their competitive analysis. Chapter 9 provides guidance on how competitive strategy should be approached in healthcare today and in the near future. It also looks at emerging and new developments in competitive strategy outside of healthcare and highlights aspects of competitive strategy approaches for healthcare organizations that will need to change as greater awareness and sophistication enters the field. Chapter 10 provides simple guidelines for implementing a higher level of competitive strategy in any healthcare organization.

I am mindful that the subject of competition is still fairly new ground for many healthcare organizations and their leaders. Particularly among executives of not-for-profit organizations, terms like competition and profit still cause some to recoil. Competition is considered to be at odds with healthcare organizations' mission to serve the needs of their communities. However, I would argue that competition sharpens the focus of the organization on the needs of its communities, allowing definition and discovery of needs that may not have been apparent before and enhancing the organization's capabilities so that it can serve identified needs better. The competitively able and fit healthcare organization will continue to be in a position to meet community needs in the future, while those less able and fit may not.

Alan M. Zuckerman, FACHE, FAAHC

# Acknowledgments

MANY TIMES DURING the two-year period it took to birth this book I thought, "why did I ever volunteer to do this?" It's not as if my life isn't already full enough with a consuming, growing management consulting practice, two teenage children who are more than happy to test me at every turn—at least when they're talking to me—and an overflowing plate of extracurricular and community activities.

Two additional concerns tormented me throughout the process. First, does anybody read anymore? More particularly, if so, is text more sophisticated than a PowerPoint© presentation obsolete? Second, will I ever finish the manuscript? The more research I did, the more I learned and the more I wrote. It was difficult to decide where to stop and how to end gracefully so as not to exhaust the reader's (already limited) patience.

This book would not have been possible without the cooperation of my family. My wife, Rita, and children, Seth and Joanna, allowed me to cut into family time to complete this project. They also allowed me to complain about how long this project was taking to finish and only occasionally told me I was boring them.

My firm also aided and abetted me throughout. In particular, Susan Arnold, my editorial assistant, did a yeoman's job in filling in the many blanks I left in the text, developing interesting case studies, and whipping the manuscript into readable shape. Christine Passaglia, my administrative assistant, transcribed hundreds of pages of barely legible longhand writing and only complained a few times about my failure to keep my promise that "the next book will be drafted on the computer."

Last, I want to thank my clients who allowed me to test some of the recommended approaches on them and tolerated me when I spoke to their management teams and boards at great length about how important competitive strategy is, often and without provocation.

# CHAPTER 1

# Competitive Strategy in Healthcare: Where Are We Now?

## INTRODUCTION

HEALTHCARE DELIVERY HAS undergone a dramatic transformation in the past 30 years, evolving from a sleepy, relatively undeveloped part of American business to a large, growing, and now significant sector of the U.S. economy. In 1970, healthcare delivery was carried out by small, locally oriented, not-for-profit hospitals; independent physicians and small medical groups; and a variety of other bit players. Healthcare delivery comprised 7.1 percent of the gross domestic product (GDP), with annual per capita healthcare expenditures of $341 (Centers for Disease Control 1999).

In 2000, healthcare spending increased 25-fold, accounting for 13.2 percent of the GDP, with annual per capita health expenditures of $4,637 (Pear 2002). Healthcare services are delivered by increasingly large organizations, both not-for-profit and for-profit, and locally, regionally, and, in some service sectors, nationally focused in scope. The physician component of healthcare delivery has been somewhat slower to organize. As of 1997, 54 percent of physicians were employed, with the number and proportion increasing every year (AMA 1998).

Although size and scale makes competitive strategy a relevant topic for healthcare providers, equally important are two other developments. First, the increasing deregulation of healthcare delivery as reflected by the abandoned or weakened certificate-of-need regulations in many states and the end of state rate regulation, except in Maryland, have ushered in an era of competition that has been absent heretofore in healthcare delivery. At the same time, excess supply of many provider types has become apparent. This oversupply is magnified by the emergence of price as an increasingly relevant factor in buyer decisions and the rise of managed care firms that have used their market power to decrease utilization and extract price concessions from nearly all providers. The resulting supply and demand imbalance in most markets sets the stage for today's competitive dynamic.

The abundance of literature on competitive strategy, both inside and outside of healthcare delivery, demonstrates that this subject is assuming growing importance throughout American industry. Also, not surprisingly, the literature is more advanced outside of healthcare delivery. Competitive strategy has been a major strategic issue for American businesses for a number of years and its significance has been heightened as nonhealthcare-delivery businesses have entered the global market.

The existence of any literature at all on competitive strategy in healthcare delivery is actually somewhat of a surprise. Until the mid-1980s, most healthcare providers struggled to keep up with growing demand. Competition was rarely overt or a critical issue except in a minority of cases. Nonetheless, competitive strategy has been a topic of interest in the academic community, and it is worthwhile to retrospectively review healthcare competitive strategy and concepts.

This chapter will summarize the relevant literature to create a framework for examining competitive strategy in healthcare delivery today. This framework will serve as an outline for presenting the state of the art in healthcare competitive strategy in the remainder of this book.

Considerable confusion exists in the literature on the seemingly simple question: what is competitive strategy? To answer this, Michael Porter (1985), one of the most prominent authorities in this area, writes:

> Competition is at the core of the success or failure of firms. Competition determines the appropriateness of a firm's activities that can contribute to its performance, such as innovations, a cohesive culture or good implementation. Competitive strategy is a search for a favorable competitive position in an industry, the fundamental arena in which competition occurs. Competitive strategy aims to establish a profitable and sustainable position against the forces that determine industry competition.

Theorists Faulkner and Bowman (1995) attempt to differentiate between corporate strategy and competitive strategy. In this construct, competitive strategy is carried out at the business-unit level, while corporate strategy is concerned with the firm overall and is applicable to those (larger) firms that consist of multiple, relatively discrete businesses.

To further the understanding of competitive strategy, Faulkner and Bowman (1995) suggest three fundamental questions to be answered in this area:

1. Where should we compete? (What markets and which segments within those markets should we concentrate on?)
2. What products should we compete with?
3. How will we gain sustainable competitive advantage in these chosen markets?

Drawing on Porter and others, Luke and Begun (1993) indicate that "[competitive] strategy is an integrating set of ideas and concepts that guide an organization in its attempts to achieve competitive advantage over its rivals." Furthermore, they state that "strategy should provide the central rallying point around which an organization's members can unite to assure that the organization survives and thrives over the long term."

Finally, Porter (1996) writes, "[C]ompetitive strategy is about being different. It is about choosing a different set of activities to deliver a unique mix of value." He addresses directly the confusion among America's business leaders about the role of operational effectiveness and strategy as competitive approaches. He argues, "[o]perational effectiveness means performing similar activities *better* than rivals perform them," while "strategic positioning means performing *different* activities from rivals' or performing similar activities in *different* ways."

The literature on competitive strategy outside of the healthcare field is abundant. Because much of the progress in thinking about competitive strategy has occurred in the general business literature, a brief summary of some of the major nonhealthcare contributions and constructs follows.

## COMPETITIVE STRATEGY OUTSIDE OF HEALTHCARE

Michael Porter undoubtedly is the most widely recognized authority on competitive strategy. Beginning with his works, *Competitive Strategy: Techniques for Analyzing Industrial Competitors* and *Competitive Advantage: Creating and Sustaining Superior Performance,* published in the early 1980s, Porter argued that companies can employ three types of generic strategies:

1. *Cost leadership*—Efficiency is emphasized to produce unit costs that are lower than competitors.
2. *Differentiation*—Distinctive competencies are used to develop unique services.
3. *Focus*—Select markets are targeted for either cost or differentiation strategies (i.e., niching).

Porter's framework emphasized the need to choose a clear competitive strategy to avoid the inherent contradictions of different strategies and thus the failure to really have any strategy at all. "Strategy is making trade-offs in competing. The essence of strategy is choosing what *not* to do. Without trade-offs, there would be no need for choice and thus no need for strategy" (Porter 1996).

Subsequently, Porter developed an expanded version of his basic model, incorporating the concept of fit—that is, developing interconnections among competitive activities so that the whole organization is stronger than the sum of its parts. He argues that "[c]ompetitive advantage grows out of the *entire* system of activities. The fit among activities substantially reduces cost or increases differentiation [or focus]" (Porter 1996).

Another approach that enjoyed great popularity in American business in the 1970s, and in healthcare to some degree thereafter, was developed by the Boston Consulting Group (BCG). BCG's framework involved dividing the company's portfolio into distinct business units, each one representing a separate product and market segment or profit center. Individual business units are characterized by their market growth rate (i.e., percent increase in revenues) and their competitive position (i.e., market share). An example of the BCG portfolio analysis for a company with nine products is illustrated in Figure 1.1. The size of each circle represents the proportion of overall organizational revenue generated by each product line.

Products or business units fall into one of four sectors:

1. *High growth/strong competitive position (the "stars"):* These business units represent the best opportunities for the company long term, but also require considerable investment.
2. *Low growth/strong competitive position (the "cash cows"):* These mature businesses can generate cash to support profitability or growth in other sectors.
3. *Low growth/weak competitive position (the "dogs"):* These units are in saturated, mature markets and can be managed for

**Figure 1.1: BCG's Growth/Share Matrix**

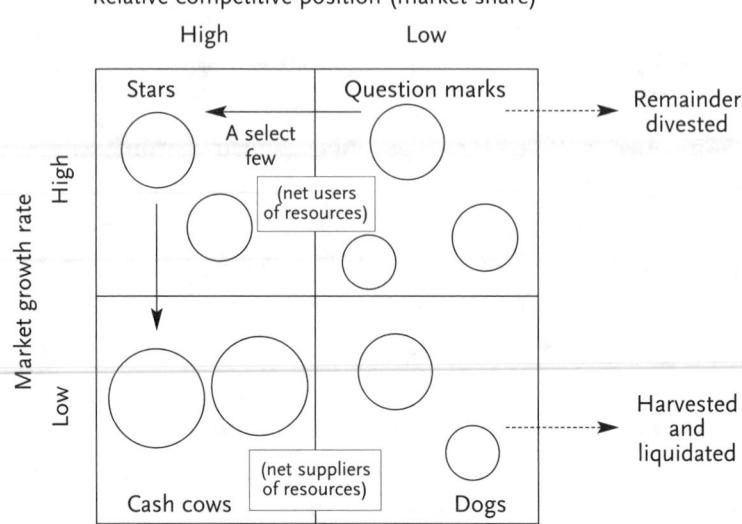

Source: Adapted from Hedley, B. 1977. "Strategy and the Business Portfolio." *Long-Range Planning* (February): 10, from *Formulation and Implementation of Competitive Strategy*, 2nd edition, by J. Pearce and R. Robinson © 1985. Reprinted with permission of The McGraw-Hill Companies.

short-term profitability, leading to likely divestiture or liquidation in the foreseeable future.

4. *High growth/weak competitive position (the "question marks"):* These high-growth business units need considerable investment for growth, but only if they have the potential to become "stars."

The goal of BCG's approach is to determine the corporate strategy that best provides a balanced portfolio of business units. BCG's ideal, balanced portfolio would have the largest sales in cash cows and stars, with only a few question marks and very few dogs, the latter with favorable cash flow (Pearce and Robinson 1985).

Competitive strategy then addresses how to implement the desired corporate approach at the business-unit level.

Subsequent improvements to the BCG approach were made by General Electric (GE). GE used multiple factors to assess industry attractiveness and business strength, rather than the single measures used by BCG, and three categories of attractiveness and strength, adding a medium category, rather than just high and low as illustrated in Figure 1.2 (Pearce and Robinson 1985). Charles Hofer further improved the BCG and GE approaches, moving from a 4-cell or 9-cell analytic grid to a 15-cell, with the latter improvement focusing on a six-stage product/market evolution framework illustrated in Figure 1.3 (Pearce and Robinson 1985). Hofer and Schendel (1978) suggest that "most corporate-level portfolio strategies are variations of one of three ideal portfolios: (1) growth portfolios, (2) project portfolios, and (3) balanced portfolios."

In the 1990s, Gary Hamel (1996) wrote extensively on corporate and competitive strategy. He suggests that three types of firms are present in any industry:

1. The "rule makers"—the companies that built the industry (e.g., Hertz, Coca-Cola) and desire to protect their dominant position.
2. The "rule takers"—the firms that appear content to play second fiddle to the industry leaders (e.g., Avis to Hertz).
3. The "rule breakers"—the firms that are rewriting the rules, overturning the established order, and revolutionizing the industry (e.g., Dell Computer versus IBM).

Hamel argues that deregulation, technological upheaval, globalization, and social change have created unprecedented conditions that are favorable to revolutionaries and hostile to incumbents. His advice is, "[u]nless you are an industry leader with an unassailable position—a status that, given the lessons of history, not even Microsoft would be wise to claim—you probably have a greater stake in staging a revolution than in preserving the status quo." Revolutionaries should look "for ways to

# Figure 1.2: General Electric's Nine-Cell Planning Grid

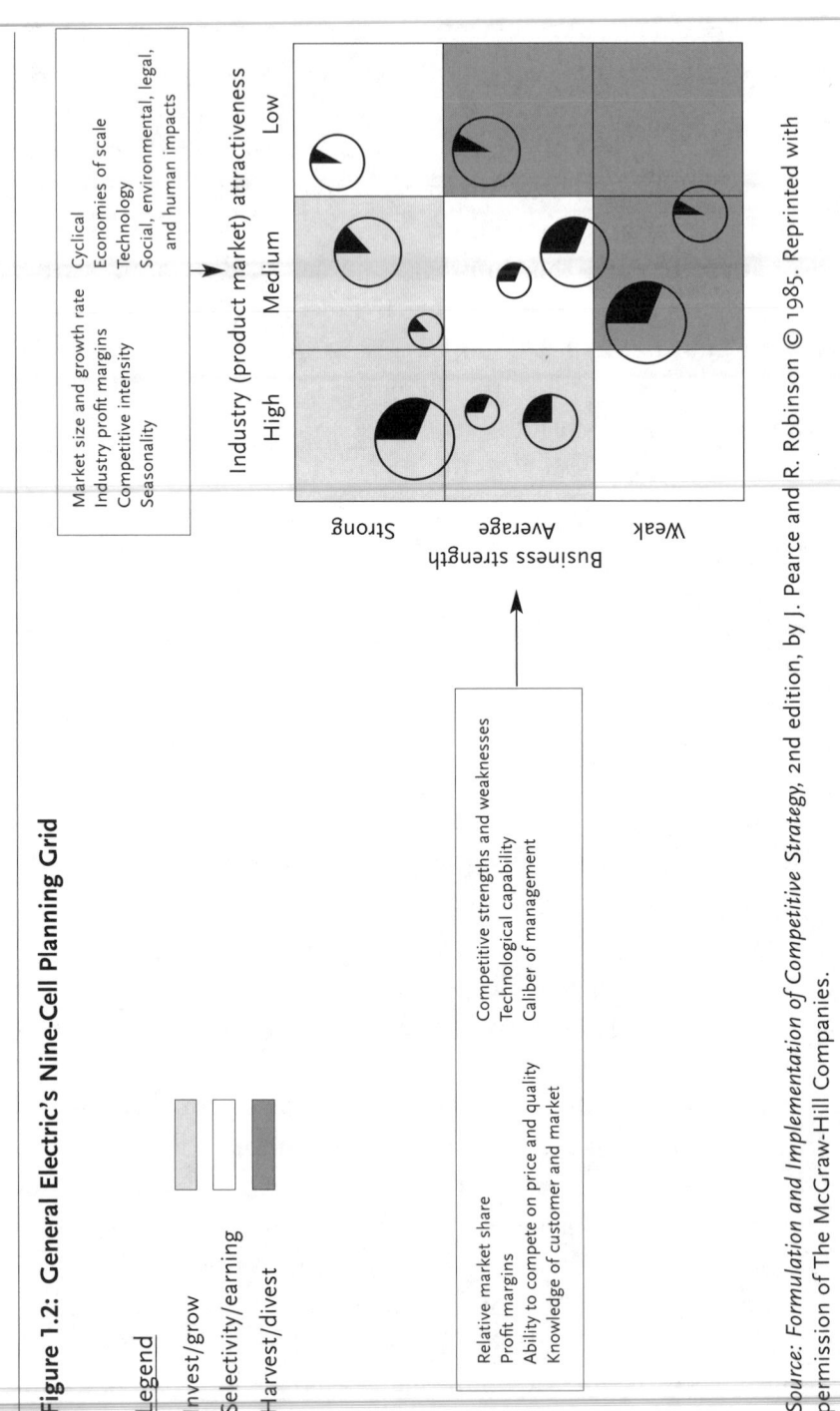

*Source: Formulation and Implementation of Competitive Strategy, 2nd edition, by J. Pearce and R. Robinson © 1985. Reprinted with permission of The McGraw-Hill Companies.*

**Figure 1.3: Product/Market-Evolution Matrix**

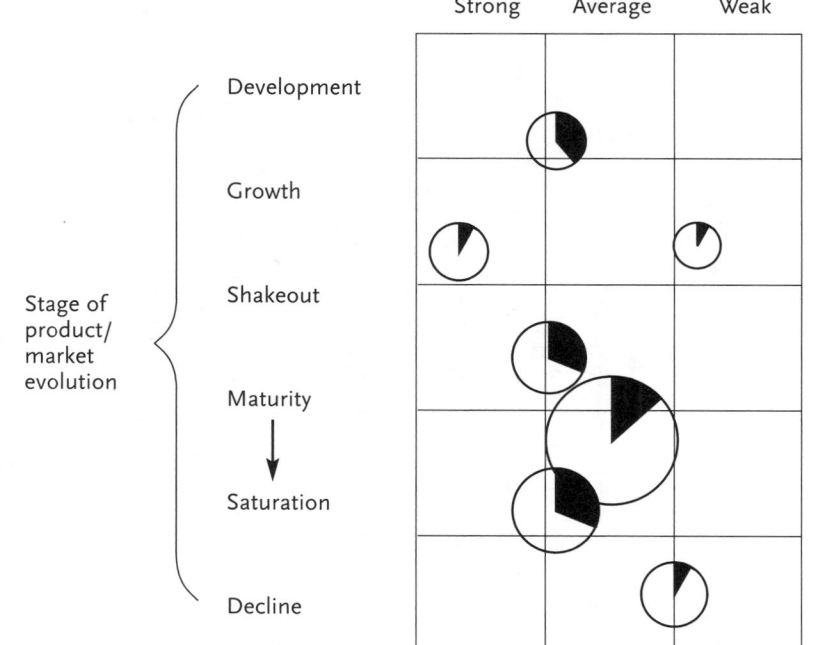

*Source:* Adapted from Hofer, C. W. 1977. "Conceptual Constructs for Formulating Corporate and Business Strategies," in *Formulation and Implementation of Competitive Strategy,* 2nd edition, by J. Pearce and R. Robinson © 1985. Reprinted with permission of The McGraw-Hill Companies.

redefine products and services, market space, and even the entire structure of an industry. . . . [P]ursuing incremental improvements while rivals reinvent the industry is like fiddling while Rome burns" (Hamel 1996).

More recently Michel Robert (1997) suggested that "no company has the resources or ability to compete against all competitors and should not attempt to do so. Instead, a company should target a few key competitors and ensure success against these. In fact, we are also of the opinion that, sometimes, competition is irrelevant." The latter is the case when markets are growing fast enough to allow all firms to grow rapidly, which was certainly the case in all of healthcare pre-1980 and possibly later and when, as Hamel suggests, the industry revolutionary is completely redefining the rules of play. In any event, Robert's basic advice is to "control the sandbox" by choosing the product and market areas in which to compete and by selecting the principal competitor(s) and managing and then neutralizing their strategy.

## COMPETITIVE STRATEGY IN HEALTHCARE

The first and possibly best known competitive strategy framework that has been used by healthcare providers was developed by Miles and Snow (1978). Although not intended exclusively or even primarily for healthcare organizations, this framework has received extensive coverage in healthcare largely due to citations in research by Shortell, Morrison, and Friedman (1980) and other leading authorities. Miles and Snow posited that organizations adopt four basic strategic postures: prospectors, analyzers, reactors, and defenders, which are illustrated in Figure 1.4 and described below in descending order of innovativeness, environmental responsiveness, and willingness to consciously assume risk and change.

*Prospectors* are entrepreneurial in nature. They are oriented toward growth and seek new product development and extension,

# Figure 1.4: Miles' and Snow's Four Organization Types

| Prospector | Analyzer | Reactor | Defender |
|---|---|---|---|
| *Problem:* How to locate and exploit new product and market opportunities | *Problem:* How to locate and exploit new product and market opportunities while simultaneously maintaining a firm base of traditional products and customers | *Problem:* How to develop a consistent set of response mechanisms to address the changing environment | *Problem:* How to "seal off" a portion of the total market to create a stable set of products and customers |
| *Solutions:* 1. Broad and continuously developing domain 2. Monitors wide range of environmental conditions and events 3. Creates change in the industry 4. Growth through product and market development 5. Growth may occur in spurts | *Solutions:* 1. Hybrid domain that is both stable and changing 2. Surveillance mechanisms mostly limited to marketing; some research and development 3. Steady growth through market penetration and product-market development | *Solutions:* 1. Clearly articulate organization's direction and strategy 2. Organization's structure and processes are shaped to fit the chosen strategy 3. Actively investigate new products/market areas and incorporate opportunities cost effectively 4. Choice between indecision or moving toward becoming Defender, Analyzer, or Prospector | *Solutions:* 1. Narrow and stable domain 2. Aggressive maintenance of domain (e.g., competitive pricing and excellent customer service) 3. Tendency to ignore developments outside of domain 4. Cautious and incremental growth primarily through market penetration 5. Some product development, but closely related to current goods or services |
| *Costs and benefits:* Product and market innovation protects the organization from a changing environment, but the organization runs the risk of low profitability and overextension of its resources | *Costs and benefits:* Low investment in research and development, combined with imitation of demonstrably successful products, minimizes risk, but domain must be optimally balanced at all times between stability and flexibility | *Costs and benefits:* Maintaining the status quo translates into ongoing instability, saturation of primary markets, and the strategic vacuum being filled by conflicting demands | *Costs and benefits:* It is difficult for competitors to dislodge the organization from its small niche in the industry, but a major shift in the market could threaten survival |

*Source: Organizational Strategy, Structure and Process,* by R. E. Miles and C. C. Snow © 1978. Reprinted with permission of The McGraw-Hill Companies.

diversification, and market penetration and extension opportunities to exploit. Prospectors are usually the market leaders.

*Analyzers* attempt to achieve a balance of innovation and stability. They often maintain stable operations in their core business, but also seek new product or market opportunities. They carefully monitor competitors and adopt behaviors and tactics that have been successfully employed by others. Analyzers thus function to some degree as market followers.

*Reactors* have no coherent strategy. They follow successful competitors, adopting their tactics and behaviors in the hopes of achieving similar benefits. They rarely change except as a result of external pressures. Their strategy, such as it is, may be characterized as mimicry.

*Defenders* attempt to protect their products and markets by maintaining stability, focusing on existing operations, and increasing efficiency. They avoid pursuit of new opportunities. They are staunch proponents of the status quo.

Luke and Begun (1993) note that "these patterns characterize not only approaches to strategy but also orientations that are often deeply embedded within an organization's culture and strategic history."

In the late 1980s and early 1990s, extensive research was conducted in hospitals using the Miles and Snow framework. The research findings concluded that many hospitals shifted during the 1980s from a defender strategy to either an analyzer or prospector strategy (Zajac and Shortell 1989; Ginn 1990). Research findings also suggested that larger hospitals and multihospital systems were more likely to adopt the more aggressive strategic orientations than smaller and independent hospitals. Furthermore, size of the organization rather than environmental conditions is the more important determinant of the choice of strategy among hospitals (Ginn and Young 1992).

In the early 1990s, Cleverley and Harvey (1992) conducted an analysis of the relationship of certain hospital strategies to performance to determine which behaviors or tactics lead to better or improved performance. In so doing, they drew on work outside of healthcare using the Profit Impact of Market Strategy (PIMS) database that empirically demonstrated the effects of market strategy on profitability of for-profit businesses outside of healthcare. Their measure of successful performance is purely financial—return on investment—and, some argue, an incomplete indicator of successful performance.

Not surprisingly, given the dominance of fixed-reimbursement payers, such as Medicare, Cleverley and Harvey found that cost control is the most important factor influencing financial performance. Of secondary importance are market share, diversification, and lower capital intensity and debt. Except possibly for the finding about capital intensity (and Cleverley and Harvey [1992] note that "newer plants do appear to attract both medical staff and patients"), a reasonable conclusion follows that lower costs, higher market share, a broader mix of services, and lower debt should be associated with better financial performance.

A similar study, using teaching hospitals only as the sample universe, was carried out subsequently by Langabeer (1998). His findings diverged from those of Cleverley and Harvey in some important ways. In particular, his analysis indicated that cost leadership (i.e., being a low-cost provider) has no influence on financial performance of teaching hospitals. Also, in contrast to the Cleverley and Harvey findings that pricing was not an important factor in hospital financial performance, Langabeer found that pricing strategy is the most important factor affecting teaching hospitals' performance. Langabeer's study did not ascribe any importance to market share in relation to financial performance. Both studies are in agreement on the importance of a product and market strategy and the prudent use of capital investments.

It is disturbing and confusing, however, that such fundamental disagreement exists about cost, pricing, and market share factors as contributors to successful performance. That the different conclusions are largely attributable to a different sample (i.e., teaching hospitals versus large urban hospitals in the Cleverley and Harvey study) is unlikely and may be more a function of other aspects of research design. The divergent findings, nonetheless, are also reflective of confusion in the field about the best path to follow.

Duncan, Ginter, and Swayne (1995) present what is probably the most complete discussion of healthcare competitive strategy available today. They discuss five levels of strategy, illustrated in Figure 1.5, that are applicable to healthcare organizations. For the purposes of this book, two of the levels are applicable to competitive strategy—the adaptive strategies and the positioning strategies. Briefly, directional strategies, as defined by Duncan, Ginter, and Swayne (1995), set future targets for the organization and are not concerned with the "how" (i.e., the strategy) to achieve the targets. Market entry strategies are actually tactics to carry out the adaptive strategies described by the authors. Operational strategies are essentially the tactics and actions to carry out the entire strategy and plan.

Duncan, Ginter, and Swayne argue that the basic decision at the adaptive strategy level is whether to expand, contract, or remain stable. If the decision is made to expand, five alternatives are available, and the competitive strategy for the organization can consist of one or more of these options, detailed in Figure 1.6:

1. *Diversification* is delving into related, unrelated, or both types of areas that appear to offer the potential for significant growth.
2. *Vertical integration* involves acquiring or developing businesses that feed or support the core enterprise. Backward vertical integration is growth toward the organization's suppliers, and forward vertical integration is growth toward the organization's buyers and consumers.
3. *Market development* is focused on increased penetration or growth into new geographic markets.
4. *Product development* is the enhancement or expansion of existing products and the introduction of new products, generally to existing markets.
5. *Penetration* is increasing market share in existing markets, generally by using current products and services.

**Figure 1.5: Hierarchy of Strategic Decisions and Alternatives**

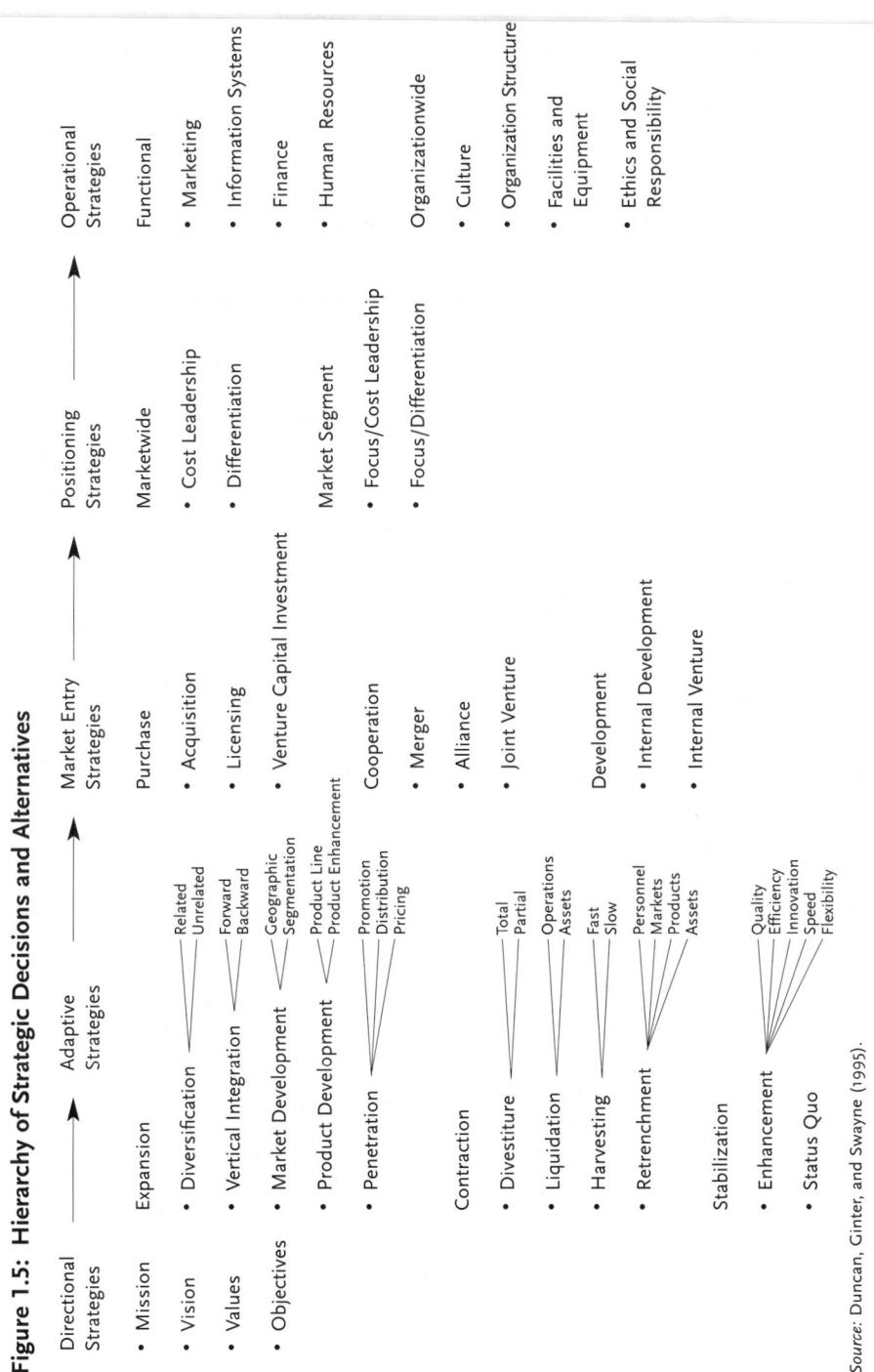

*Source:* Duncan, Ginter, and Swayne (1995).

## Figure 1.6: Rationales and Relative Risks of Expansion Strategic Alternatives

| Strategy | Relative Risk | Rationale |
| --- | --- | --- |
| Related Diversification | Moderate | • Pursuit of high-growth markets<br>• Entering less-regulated segments<br>• Cannot achieve current objectives<br>• Synergy is possible from new business<br>• Offset seasonal or cyclical influences |
| Unrelated Diversification | High | • Pursuit of high-growth markets<br>• Entering less-regulated segments<br>• Cannot achieve current objectives<br>• Current markets are saturated or in decline<br>• Organization has excess cash<br>• Antitrust regulations prohibit expansion in current industry<br>• Tax loss may be acquired |
| Backward Vertical Integration | High | • Control the flow of patients through the system<br>• Scarcity of raw materials or essential inventory/supplies<br>• Deliveries are unreliable<br>• Lack of materials or supplies will shut down operations<br>• Price or quality of materials or supplies variable<br>• Industry/market seen as profitable for long period |
| Forward Vertical Integration | High | • Control the flow of patients through the system<br>• Faster delivery required<br>• High level of coordination required between one stage and another<br>• Industry/market seen as profitable for long period |

**FIGURE 1.6** *(continued)*

| | | |
|---|---|---|
| Market Development (geographic and segmentation) | Moderate | • New markets are available for present products<br>• New markets may be served efficiently<br>• Expected high revenues<br>• Organization has cost leadership advantage<br>• Organization has differentiation advantage<br>• Current market is growing |
| Product Development (product line and product enhancement) | Moderate | • Currently in strong market but product is weak or product line incomplete<br>• Market tastes are changing<br>• Product technology is changing<br>• Maintenance or creation of differentiation advantage |
| Penetration (promotion, distribution, and pricing) | Moderate | • Present market is growing<br>• Product/service innovation will extend market of product life cycle<br>• Expected revenues are high<br>• Organization has cost leadership advantage<br>• Organization has differentiation advantage |

*Source:* Duncan, Ginter, and Swayne (1995).

Duncan, Ginter, and Swayne (1995) suggest that diversification and vertical integration are strategies best applied at the corporate level and enterprisewide, while market development, product development, and penetration are appropriate at the business unit level as they largely apply to competition within a given market. Thus, corporate strategies materially increase the scope of services of the organization, while divisional strategies principally expand current operations.

If the decision is made to contract, one or more of four main alternatives can be pursued as illustrated in Figure 1.7:

**Figure 1.7: Rationales and Relative Risks of Contraction Strategic Alternatives**

| Strategy | Relative Risk | Rationale |
|---|---|---|
| Divestiture | Low | • Industry in long-term decline<br>• Cash needed to enter new, higher-growth area<br>• Lack of expected synergy with core operation<br>• Required investment in new technology seen as too high<br>• Too much regulation |
| Liquidation | Low | • Organization can no longer operate<br>• Bankruptcy<br>• Trim/reduce assets<br>• Superseded by new technology |
| Harvesting | Low | • Late maturity/decline state of the product life cycle<br>• Considering divestiture or downsizing<br>• Short-term cash needed |
| Retrenchment (personnel, markets, products, assets) | Moderate | • Market has become too diverse<br>• Market is too geographically spread out<br>• Personnel costs are too high<br>• Too many products or services<br>• Marginal or nonproductive facilities |

*Source:* Duncan, Ginter, and Swayne (1995).

1. *Divestiture* generally involves the sale of a business unit as a result of a decision to leave the market in which the unit is operating. Outsourcing, increasingly used by healthcare organizations, is one form of divestiture.

2. *Liquidation,* or the selling of the individual assets of a business unit, is employed when the value of the parts is worth more than the whole.

3. *Harvesting* is applicable to a market in long-term decline. It involves maintaining the business unit as the market declines and, with little or no investment, maximizes short-term profitability.
4. *Retrenchment* often occurs after a period of rapid growth and involves a redefinition of the target market, selective cost elimination, and asset reduction.

Duncan, Ginter, and Swayne (1995) suggest that divestiture and liquidation are appropriate corporate-level strategies, whereas harvesting and retrenchment are strategies usually focused at the division level.

Stabilization strategies are used by organizations that are operating and progressing satisfactorily. In these cases, few changes in the target markets or products or services are necessary. The two stabilization strategies are both applicable largely at the divisional level, as shown in Figure 1.8:

1. *Enhancement* is an appropriate strategy in those situations when the organization is doing well but could benefit from minor improvements in existing operations.
2. *Status quo* strategies may be appropriate in mature, stable markets and involve defending the business unit's position to maintain market share and profitability.

Duncan, Ginter, and Swayne's presentation of positioning strategies follows Porter's framework of the three generic strategies (cost leadership, differentiation, and focus) discussed earlier in this chapter. They argue that at this level, strategy is focused on how the organization's products and services are positioned in the market versus the competitors, using one of the three strategies advocated by Porter, as illustrated in Figure 1.9.

Luke and Begun (1993) attempt to synthesize the competitive strategy literature into a three-part framework. They suggest three sources of competitive advantage:

**Figure 1.8: Rationales and Relative Risks of Stabilization Strategic Alternatives**

| Strategy | Relative Risk | Rationale |
|---|---|---|
| Enhancement (quality, efficiency, innovation, speed, and flexibility) | Low | • Organization has operational inefficiencies<br>• Need to lower costs<br>• Need to improve quality<br>• Improve internal processes |
| Status Quo | Low | • Maintain market share position<br>• Maturity/late maturity stage of the product life cycle<br>• Product/market generating cash but has little potential for future growth<br>• Extremely competitive market |

*Source:* Duncan, Ginter, and Swayne (1995).

1. *Position or value-oriented strategies.* Similar to the Porter generic strategies (cost, leadership, differentiation, and focus) described earlier, these types of competitive strategies are based on one of three factors: low cost, high differentiation, or focus/niche.

2. *Pace or timing/intensity strategies.* Similar in some respects to the Miles and Snow categorization of four types of strategic orientation also described earlier, these competitive strategies rely on the timing and intensity of action to gain advantage.

3. *Power or size-related strategies.* Most of the growth strategies described previously by Duncan, Ginter, and Swayne are power strategies, relying on size to create economies and market power to create advantage.

Furthermore, they argue that the appropriateness of applying each of these types of competitive strategies varies based on the nature of the market in which the firm is operating (see Figure 1.10). In particular, the degree of seller concentration is the most important

**Figure 1.9: Porter's Matrix**

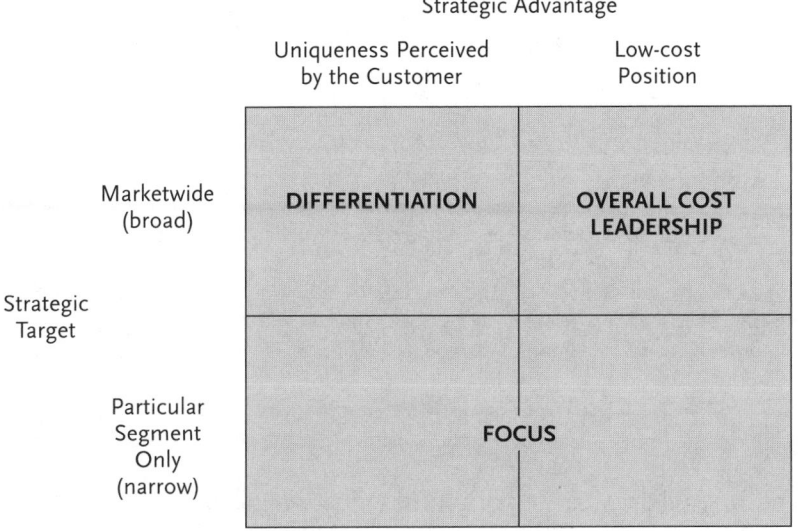

*Sources:* Duncan, Ginter, and Swayne (1995) and Porter (1980).

dimension affecting the potential for success of the competitive strategy type chosen. Here, too, are three relevant categories:

1. atomistic: many small sellers,
2. oligopolistic: a few large sellers, and
3. monopolistic: a single seller.

In most atomistic markets, Luke and Begun indicate that position or value-oriented strategies are most likely to lead to competitive advantage because of the fragmented market. The issue for the firm is how to begin to rise above the fray by differentiating its products in a crowded market.

In oligopolistic markets, firms seek to improve their position relative to other typically large, threatening competitors. In such situations, power strategies are more likely to be employed to gain

**Figure 1.10: Three Sources of Competitive Advantage in Each of the Three Market Types**

| | Power | Pace | Position |
|---|---|---|---|
| Atomistic | L | M | H |
| Oligopolistic | H | M | L |
| Monopolistic | L | L | L |

*Note:* L = low, M = medium, H = high levels of importance, differentiated by degree of seller concentration.
*Source:* Luke and Begun (1993). From *Health Care Management Organization Design and Behavior*, 3rd edition, by S. M. Shortell and A. D. Kaluzny © 1993. Reprinted with permission of Delmar, a division of Thomson Learning. Fax 800-730-2215.

or increase dominance both for the firm overall and in its key business lines.

Finally, the monopolist, by definition, has no active competitors and does not need to place emphasis on any strategy type in particular. Few true monopolists exist among healthcare providers, and this category has little applicability to the situation faced by the overwhelming majority in the field.

## RESEARCH SUMMARY AND IMPLICATIONS

The research suggests three general categories within which to view general competitive strategy and competitive strategy for healthcare firms in particular: (1) corporate versus product and market, (2) growth versus nongrowth, and (3) behavioral.

### Corporate Versus Product and Market

Many firms have an overall corporate competitive strategy orientation that is consistent across all products and markets in which they operate, whereas some firms, particularly larger and more diverse companies, may carry out completely different competitive strategies in different business units. In general, smaller organizations have a more unified competitive strategy than larger ones. In healthcare, while some differences in competitive strategy are present at the product and market levels in larger organizations, in general, the overall corporate competitive strategy orientation carries through fairly consistently to the operating units.

## Growth Versus Nongrowth

Duncan, Ginter, and Swayne are leading proponents of the growth versus nongrowth framework to explain the competitive orientation of healthcare organizations. While this framework has clear applicability at the product and market levels, it is less useful for explaining overall corporate competitive strategy. Few, if any, organizations are likely to consciously adopt an overall posture of contraction, at least if they expect to stay in business for very long. Stabilization may be a strategic alternative (similar to the *defender* in the Miles and Snow typology), but it, too, is not one that bodes well for long-term success or even viability. Thoughtful corporate competitive strategy must contain a growth or at least an enhancement orientation; otherwise, it cannot meet the test of the definitions of competitive strategy discussed earlier in this chapter.

## Behavioral

The prospector, analyzer, reactor, and defender framework developed by Miles and Snow and Hamel's rule makers, rule takers, and rule breakers framework are both examples of what may be characterized as behavioral competitive strategy frameworks. In these cases, the psyche of the organization forms the basis for the overall competitive strategy, rather than a more analytically derived alternative. It is not surprising that a framework such as that of

Miles and Snow has been used extensively in characterizing competitive strategy of not-for-profit healthcare organizations, since these organizations have primarily served single, local markets and are deeply rooted in their history and culture.

## CONCLUSION

The changes taking place in healthcare in the past five to ten years have dramatically altered the historical behaviors of healthcare organizations. All forecasts of the future indicate that the rate of change is likely to continue and probably accelerate. The increasingly dynamic environment mandates having a strategy and particularly a competitive strategy more essential than ever. And this type of environment deems maintenance and stabilization or contraction competitive strategies infeasible. In fact, the healthcare market is moving more toward the freer market of corporate America, and successful organizations must adopt the more sophisticated competitive strategies of for-profit corporations to survive and thrive in this new era.

Some of this new competitive behavior is already taking place in healthcare. To set the stage for the new competitive strategy models of the twenty-first century, understanding how some of the leading healthcare organizations in the United States have already modified their competitive strategy to adapt to the new environment is important.

In the next six chapters, aspects of the strategic frameworks discussed in this chapter are used to profile the principal competitive strategies being employed today inside and outside of the healthcare industry. The chapters address particular competitive strategies including examples of their application in organizations.

The final three chapters summarize lessons learned from current, leading-edge healthcare organizations' behavior and the latest business research to suggest where healthcare competitive strategy is headed early in the twenty-first century.

# REFERENCES

American Medical Association and the Center for Health Policy Research. 1998. *Socioeconomic Characteristics of Medical Practice 1997/98*, p. 18. Chicago: American Medical Association.

Centers for Disease Control. 1999. [Online report retrieved July 21, 2000.] http://www.cdc.gov/nchs/fastats/pdf/hu99t116.pdf.

Cleverley, W. O., and R. K. Harvey. 1992. "Competitive Strategy for Successful Hospital Management." *Hospital and Health Services Administration* 37 (1): 53–69.

Duncan, W. J., P. M. Ginter, and L. E. Swayne. 1995. *Strategic Management of Health Care Organizations*, 2nd Edition, Boston: Blackwell Business.

Faulkner, D., and C. Bowman. 1995. *The Essence of Competitive Strategy*, p. 2. Upper Saddle River, NJ: Prentice Hall.

Ginn, G. O. 1990. "Strategic Adaptation in the Hospital Industry: An Examination of the Response of the Acute Care Hospital to the Turbulent Environment of the 1980s." *Health Services Research* 26 (4): 565–91.

Ginn, G. O., and G. J. Young. 1992. "Organizational and Environmental Determinants of Hospital Strategy." *Hospital and Health Services Administration* 37 (3): 291–302.

Hamel, G. 1996. "Strategy as Revolution." *Harvard Business Review* July/August: 69–82.

Hofer, C., and D. Schendel. 1978. *Strategy Formulation: Analytical Concepts*. St. Paul, Minnesota: West Publishing, in Pearce and Robinson, op cit. p. 253.

Langabeer, J. 1998. "Competitive Strategy in Turbulent Healthcare Markets: An Analysis of Financially Effective Teaching Hospitals." *Journal of Healthcare Management* 43 (6): 512–25.

Luke, R. D., and J. W. Begun. 1993. "Strategy Making in Health Care Organizations." In *Health Care Management: Organization Design and Behavior*, 3rd edition, edited by S. Shortell and A. Kaluzny. Albany, NY: Delmar.

Miles, R. E., and C. C. Snow. 1978. *Organizational Strategy, Structure and Process*. New York: McGraw-Hill.

Pear, R. 2002. "Propelled by Drug and Hospital Costs, Health Spending Surged in 2000." *New York Times*, January 8. [Online article.] http://www.nytimes.com.

Pearce, J., and R. Robinson. 1985. *Formulation and Implementation of Competitive Strategy*, 2nd edition, pp. 247, 250–53. New York: McGraw-Hill.

Porter, M. 1985. *Competitive Advantage: Creating and Sustaining Superior Performance*, p. 1. New York: Simon and Schuster Trade.

Porter, M. 1996. "What is Strategy?" *Harvard Business Review* November/December: 62, 64, 70, 73.

———. 1980. *Competitive Strategy: Techniques for Analyzing Industries and Competitors.* New York: The Free Press, a division of MacMillan, Inc.

Robert, M. 1997. *Strategy Pure & Simple II,* p. 143. New York: McGraw-Hill.

Shortell, S. M., E. M. Morrison, and B. Friedman. 1990. *Strategic Choices for America's Hospitals: Managing Change in Turbulent Times.* San Francisco: Jossey-Bass.

Zajac, E. J., and S. M. Shortell. 1989. "Changing Generic Strategies: Likelihood, Direction and Performance Implications." *Strategic Management Journal* 10 (5): 413–30.

# CHAPTER 2

# Vertical Integration

## INTRODUCTION

VERTICAL INTEGRATION HAS been a popular and widely applied competitive strategy. Outside of healthcare, organizations have experienced variable success with this strategy, as exhibited by the many mergers and acquisitions of the late 1990s. In the healthcare industry, organizations have struggled to realize the purported benefits of vertical integration.

This chapter examines vertical integration, including its competitive advantages, and presents examples of how vertical integration has been applied outside of healthcare and within healthcare organizations.

## VERTICAL INTEGRATION DEFINED

Vertical integration is the joining together of complementary, mutually dependent businesses or business units, operating in different parts of an industry, into one coordinated enterprise. The intent of vertical integration is to create an enterprise that has control of customer (forward vertical integration) and supplier (backward vertical integration) relationships, although some enterprises may control only customer or only supplier relationships.

In healthcare, the merger of hospitals with nursing homes, home care agencies, physician practices, and other healthcare organizations to create a vertically integrated delivery organization has been one of the most common phenomena in the past decade. In some instances, these organizations have also developed insurance products to further integrate the enterprise. Less common among healthcare organizations are backward integration relationships. Vertical integration is typically achieved, both in healthcare and other industries, through merger or acquisition, but can be accomplished through internal strategies to create a business unit that will be integrated.

While vertical integration in industry most frequently occurs through full-asset mergers, strategic alliances have become an increasingly popular form of integration. Conrad and Dowling (1990) discuss nine ways to accomplish vertical integration in healthcare:

1.  Internal development of new services
2.  Acquisition of another organization's services
3.  Formal merger
4.  Lease or sale/lease-back arrangement
5.  Franchise
6.  Joint venture
7.  Contractual agreement
8.  Loan guarantee
9.  Informal agreement or affiliation

## VERTICAL INTEGRATION AS A COMPETITIVE ADVANTAGE

The competitive advantages of vertical integration typically fall into one of three categories: control of the customer, better service, and economies of operations. In forward vertical integration, control of the customer gives the enterprise a greater ability to expose and direct customers to use the organization's related business units. The competitive advantage of improved service is achieved by combining and coordinating related complementary entities to provide more ready access and easier availability to customers who require more than one product or service; in healthcare, this approach is often referred to as seamless care or one-stop shopping. For healthcare organizations, these first two aspects of vertical integration have been viewed as ways to decrease the need for externally oriented competitive strategy while focusing one's strategy internally on maximizing cross-referrals among business units. The potential competitive benefits of economies of operations in backward integration are predictable demands for suppliers that eliminate potential waste and thus lower unit costs. In forward integration, the benefits of economies of operations may occur from sharing administrative and overhead costs.

Another frequently cited benefit of vertical integration is market power. The sheer size of a vertically related enterprise may provide advantages in terms of leverage with buyers and image among consumers. Also, similar to horizontal integration, which is discussed in chapter 3, forward vertical integration provides the organization with more contacts with patients and greater visibility, potentially leading to a higher profile and image, and ultimately, more business. Lastly, also similar to horizontal integration, potential clinical synergies generated by the combined expertise of individuals and organizations involved in the delivery of care could lead to new or expanded capabilities and cross-referrals.

Vertical integration has demonstrated variable success as a common competitive strategy outside of healthcare delivery. The 1970s and 1980s witnessed waves of popularity for vertical integration. More recently, vertical integration experienced somewhat of a resurgence in the late 1990s as a flurry of mergers and acquisitions took place, although most of this activity was horizontal in nature. Vertical integration has been a particularly popular vehicle for organizations seeking to control the customer, improve service, and realize economies of operations.

Porter (1980) reviews the strategic rationale for vertical integration in his seminal work, *Competitive Strategy*. He writes that vertical integration "represents a decision by the firm to utilize internal or administrative transactions rather than market transactions to accomplish its economic purposes." Clearly, nearly all firms are vertically integrated to some degree, since few, if any, have all of their functions performed by independent economic contractors. Firms obviously find having some portion of their administrative, production, distribution, and marketing processes performed in-house advantageous and thus achieve some level of vertical integration.

For the for-profit company, Porter (1980) describes the main benefits of vertical integration, at least in theory, as the economies it generates. He defines five categories of economies resulting from combined operations, internal control and coordination, information, avoiding the market, and stable relationships.

In addition to these economic benefits, Porter (1980) suggests five other important strategic benefits from vertical integration: improved ability to differentiate the product, access to distribution channels, better access to market information, higher price realization, and protection of proprietary knowledge.

Despite the potential benefits of vertical integration, Porter (1980) also describes the problems of realizing the benefits of vertical integration and presents examples of successful and unsuccessful vertical integration efforts. He summarizes the major common misperceptions of the benefits of vertical integration as follows:

- A strong market position in one stage can automatically be extended to the other.
- Internal control is always cheaper.
- Vertical integration into a competitive business often makes sense.

- Vertical integration can save a strategically sick business.
- Experience in one part of the vertical chain automatically qualifies management to direct upstream or downstream units.

## VERTICAL INTEGRATION CASE STUDIES

Several current examples from recent vertical integration situations may help to illustrate some of Porter's points about the benefits and pitfalls of this strategy.

### AT&T Corporation

In October 2000, the AT&T Corporation announced it was launching its third major restructuring since 1984. This move initiates the widely anticipated dismantling of the telephone and cable giant that cost more than $100 billion to create and confirms that the corporation is restructuring its vision of one-stop shopping for communications services, including Internet access, web hosting, IT outsourcing, global infrastructure, wireless communications, and platforms for application service providers.

The current restructuring plan, expected to be completed in 2002, will create four distinct, publicly held companies: a cable company (AT&T Broadband), a wireless company (AT&T Wireless), a subsidiary to run the telecommunications network and serve business customers (AT&T Business), and a unit to handle consumer long-distance business (AT&T Consumer) (Meyerson 2000).

National AT&T advertising announcing the merger stated, "The great promise of this restructuring is that it will free the new companies to move faster—to be quicker to meet customer needs, and more swift to seize growth opportunities." An AT&T press release cites the example of AT&T Wireless being established as an asset-based stock company with the ability to raise more capital than it could as part of AT&T, which should in turn give AT&T Wireless more strategic flexibility (AT&T 2000a).

The latest move is a departure from the traditional vertical integration strategy that has dominated AT&T's history. In 1997, with increased competition and falling prices threatening AT&T's long-distance business, new chief executive C. Michael Armstrong envisioned AT&T as a hub for telephone, television, and Internet services (Meyerson 2000). This move included efforts to return to the local phone business AT&T abandoned in a 1984 court-ordered breakup that resulted in the spin-off of local calling operations as seven Baby Bells.

To control both the customer and supplier ends of the market, AT&T sought to acquire its own direct connections with homes and businesses rather than pay the Baby Bells to use their phone lines. AT&T proceeded to purchase Tele-Communications, Inc., and MediaOne Group, two of the nation's largest cable companies. Although the move boosted AT&T's share price to record highs in early 2000, stock prices fell off in the following six months as it became apparent that long-distance prices were falling faster than expected. The resulting losses spoiled AT&T's revenue projections and inhibited its ability to upgrade the cable systems for two-way communication (Meyerson 2000).

### Can Supercarriers Successfully Deliver?

While many industry experts touted the great promise of the ambitious one-stop shopping strategy, customers have questioned whether supercarriers like AT&T and MCI WorldCom are taking on more than they can successfully deliver. Melding the disparate services and products that are the legacy of megamergers into single offerings demands massive integration initiatives that may be slow to yield anticipated benefits.

Users have claimed that basic support services have suffered as the supercarriers have diluted their efforts by spreading themselves too thin. Others claim that some of the best technical and customer service professionals are fired or resign with each merger. These weaknesses have opened up opportunities for other competitors, such as the Baby Bells, to threaten the supercarriers' core competencies (Wallace 2000).

In addition to the 1984 Baby Bell spin-off and current restructuring plans, AT&T split itself into three companies in 1996—the largest voluntary break-up in the history of American business. Its communications equipment arm and Bell Labs research unit joined to form the $20 billion Lucent Technologies, Inc. Its computer division was spun off as NCR Corporation to focus on retailing, financial services, and communications. The remaining communications and information services company with approximately $51 billion in annual revenue retained the AT&T name and grew to include wireless and credit card businesses (Allen 1996).

Massive shifts in employee numbers have resulted with each restructuring. Prior to the 1984 breakup, AT&T had 964,000 employees. With the spin-off of the Baby Bells, the corporation was left with 373,000 workers. In 1996, more than half of AT&T's employees left with Lucent or NCR. At the time of the October 2000 restructuring, AT&T had 163,600 employees, with nearly a third of those employees working in the cable broadband division (Meyerson 2000).

AT&T's chief, Armstrong, claims that the latest corporate restructuring is not a contradiction to his one-stop shopping strategy, stating that the new companies will move faster to meet customer needs while serving under a recognized and respected brand name. He also points out that the separate companies will continue to collaborate and offer bundled services through intercompany agreements (Meyerson 2000). AT&T Business will bundle AT&T Wireless services into its services for business companies and will also continue to use AT&T Broadband cable systems to serve some customers. Through competitive, long-term commercial contracts, the Wireless, Broadband, and Consumer companies will purchase network services from AT&T Business (AT&T 2000b).

Indeed, throughout the history of AT&T, which reaches back to 1875 with founder Alexander Graham Bell's invention of the telephone, the vertical integration strategy is apparent. According to Robert E. Allen, former chairman and chief executive officer of AT&T, "AT&T literally began with the invention of the telephone and a vertical integration strategy that became the heart of our very culture. From the beginning, AT&T set out to supply the phones, the network equipment and the services in what quickly became the finest telecommunications system in the world." Allen states that the company retained the strategy even after the 1984 spin-off of local telephone companies, as the firm stayed in the phone equipment and long-distance businesses and eventually moved into the computer business in 1991 when AT&T acquired NCR in a $7.3 billion merger (Allen 1996).

Allen claims that the 1996 split-off of Lucent and NCR resulted from the realization that the whole was less than the sum of its parts as the corporation had reached the point where the advantages of size and scope were being offset by the time and cost of coordinating and integrating business strategies that were in conflict. For example, AT&T's service businesses were competing with the same companies that were the best customers or potential customers of AT&T's equipment manufacturing businesses. With few synergies in existence between the communications and manufacturing businesses, Allen stated that the 1996 split-up was above all else a strategic restructuring to give each of the new companies a chance to take advantage of "enormous global opportunities" (Allen 1996).

For most of AT&T's history as a regulated monopoly, the corporation was insulated from market pressures. It has only been since the 1984 split-off of the Baby Bells that the corporation has had to transition from monopoly to direct competition. And the competition has become fierce. Long-distance telephone services alone have become intensely competitive. AT&T's long-distance market share fell from more than 90 percent in 1984 to around 50 percent in 1996. New technologies, primarily fiber optic transmission, have also challenged the corporation, with an increasing percentage of transmissions taking the form of data rather than conversations (AT&T 2000b).

Time will tell if AT&T's latest restructuring is capable of withstanding fierce competition and can keep pace with new technology or if the corporation returns to its more traditional roots of vertical integration or another corporate structure.

## The Walt Disney Company

The Walt Disney Company is a multimedia powerhouse that emerged from the small animation studio Walt Disney founded in 1928. Ranked as the number three media conglomerate (behind AOL Time Warner and Viacom) with over $25 billion in revenue in 2000 and over $10 billion in assets (Hoovers.com 2001a), Disney has organized its businesses into three divisions that contribute roughly equally in revenue: content, broadcasting, and theme parks.

In the content division, Disney owns a number of cable television networks that create original programming, such as the Disney Channel, ESPN, Lifetime, A&E, and the History Channel. Also within the content division are companies called "Filmed Entertainment," including Touchstone, Miramax, and Buena Vista International. Within the Buena Vista Music Group, Disney owns a number of record labels and sheet-music publishers. Disney also owns Hyperion book publishers and publishes *ESPN* magazine, *FamilyFun Magazine,* and *Discover* magazine.

Disney's Internet Group operates within the content division, running sites such as disney.com, espn.com, and abcnews.com. The content division is additionally responsible for Walt Disney

Feature Animation, Walt Disney Theatrical Productions, Disney Interactive, and Disney Consumer Products, including the Disney Stores and ESPN the Store.

The theme parks and resort division runs the well-known Disneyland parks in California, Florida, Paris, and Tokyo. The Disney Cruise Line and Walt Disney Imagineering are also run out of this division, as well as Disney Regional Entertainment, which features franchised clubs and arcades such as Club Disney and ESPNZone.

Disney's holdings include the vast ABC television network and ten television stations (FAIR 2000). The corporation also owns the ABC radio network with about 30 stations nationwide and has broadcasting ventures such as Radio Disney, Buena Vista Television, and the ESPN network. In addition to Disney's three main divisions, the corporation participates in joint ventures with other major media companies such as AOL Time Warner and PBS.

Clearly just a description of Disney's holdings demonstrates how the company has used vertical integration to become a media giant. In fact, Disney illustrates Porter's five strategic benefits of vertical integration mentioned earlier in this chapter: improved ability to differentiate the product, access to distribution channels, better access to market information, higher price realization, and protection of proprietary knowledge.

Disney has not only dominated U.S. media markets but has emerged from the 1990s as a global media giant. Disney generated about 15 percent of its income outside of the United States in 1990 (McChesney 1997). By 1997 that figure had jumped to the 30 to 35 percent range, with expectations that the majority of Disney's business would be abroad during the first decade of the twenty-first century (McChesney 1997). This growth would be achieved from joint ventures with local firms and other global powerhouses, leveraging these initiatives through the Disney Channel and ESPN International. These expectations may be scaled back as volatile economic conditions overseas have forced downsizing in the company's international operations, primarily in Asia. In 1998, revenues from international sources, including U.S. exports, accounted for only 21 percent of total company revenues (Disney 1999).

*Shutting Out the Competition*

As Disney almost tripled in size in the 1990s, it has literally shut out firms that cannot compete against its conglomerated media holdings and has so dominated the markets by its sheer size that competitors cannot come close to buying Disney out. With interests in film production, book and magazine publishing, television channels and a network, radio stations, retail stores, and amusement parks, Disney as a whole is considerably greater than the sum of its parts. For example, a Disney film may generate a soundtrack, a book, toys and clothing, a spin-off television show, CD-ROMs, video games, and amusement park rides.

Disney's path to becoming a media giant began in the early 1990s as the corporation shifted emphasis from resorts and theme parks to the film and television divisions. The 1995 acquisition of Capital Cities/ABC for $19 billion, one of the largest acquisitions in business history (McChesney 1997), was viewed as the crown jewel of Disney's vertically integrated television empire and clinched Disney's move as a challenger to AOL Time Warner's status as the world's largest media firm. Already established as a pioneer in cross-selling and promotion, the ABC acquisition added a broadcasting network and global media holdings to Disney's substantial arsenal. An August 1995 article in *Advertising Age* stated that Disney "is uniquely positioned to fulfill any marketing option, on any scale almost anywhere in the world" (McChesney 1997).

The ABC acquisition was not the first venture between ABC and Disney. In the early 1950s, ABC and Disney struck a deal to raise the capital Walt Disney needed to build Disneyland. In exchange for a 34 percent interest in the business and loan guarantees, Disney agreed to produce a weekly program called *Disneyland* for ABC. No other studio had made the foray into television, but for Disney it was the beginning of a synergy that still exists today among all of Disney's business interests. When the park opened in 1955, the television show became an advertisement for the parks and Disney films (Stone 1993) and spurred the formation of the Disney empire.

### The Dangers of Concentrated Power

The Disney magic has not emerged without rebuke. Critics of dominant players like Disney and AOL Time Warner are concerned about concentrated media power, not only for the companies' individual strength but also for their active pursuit of equity joint ventures with their "competitors" whereby they reduce competition and risk by sharing ownership of projects.

Despite Disney's demonstrated success, not all of its joint ventures have been amicable. In October 1998, the Children's Broadcasting Corporation (CBC) was awarded $20 million in a lawsuit against ABC Radio Networks, Inc., and the Walt Disney Company. The jury concluded that ABC and Disney failed to perform under a strategic alliance and used what they had learned to launch their own children's radio service. According to Christopher Dahl, president of CBC, "It was almost in a premeditated way that they tried to run us out of business. This doesn't happen very often where a little company can prove a big company did something wrong" (Communications Media Center at New York Law School 1998).

Consumer watchdog groups, such as the Center for Media Education, question how Disney's now multinational corporation with interests around the world will affect news decisions and inhibit diversity of media ownership (Center for Media Education 1995). Others have criticized Disney for their infamous focus on employee loyalty. Not long after the 1995 acquisition of ABC, Jim Hightower, a radio talk show host whose program was distributed by ABC, experienced a harsher side of the "mouse." Hightower was known for taking on big corporations and their Washington, DC allies. Despite his estimated audience of 1.5 million listeners on some 150 stations nationwide, Hightower was fired following remarks critical of the Disney acquisition of ABC, ABC News' deferral to tobacco companies in the face of a lawsuit, and Disney's employment of homeless contract workers (FAIR 1995). Although Disney claimed the firing was not tied to Hightower's comments, similar firings also followed reports of criticisms of Disney CEO Michael Eisner and other Disney executives and reports of stories being pulled from ABC's news programs due to content critical of Disney business practices.

Eisner, Disney CEO since 1984, is touted as the visionary behind the Disney explosion and is credited with saving Disney from its decline that started with Walt Disney's death in 1966. Eisner set in motion policies that recreated the synergy among the Disney films, theme parks, merchandising, animation, and television. Eisner's commitment to keeping the corporation vertical can be seen in the simple decision not to allow the purchase of park-hopping passports (that allow guests to "hop" between parks in one day), unless guests are registered at Disney hotels. By controlling the entire Disney experience (lodging, meals, merchandising, and entertainment), the company seeks to keep guests' money within the confines of its theme parks.

### Disney as a Financial Powerhouse

Disney financial performance has been impressive. From 1985 to 1998, Disney's annualized earnings growth was 20 percent (Eisner 2000), although revenue growth has slowed recently. Disney CFO Thomas Skaggs expects earnings beyond 2001 to grow 13 to 15 percent annually (Reuters Company News 2001).

But not all Disney ventures are charmed. From 1995 to 1999, the ABC network lost 35 percent of its viewers (Adalian 1999). A flurry of management and programming changes has ensued to shore up lagging viewership.

In January 2001, Disney shut down GO.com, with 400 employees losing their jobs. GO.com was a separately traded common stock that was the portal for the Disney Internet Group (Fisher 2001). Shutting down GO.com, which Michael Eisner states is the most difficult decision he has had to make, will result in a non-cash write-off of intangible assets of $790 million, with severance and other write-offs accounting for $25 to $50 million (Fisher 2001). According to Eisner, the Disney web sites will now benefit from closer ties to the parent company as new areas of the Internet, such as video-on-demand (to be dubbed "MovieBox"), interactive television, and broadband initiatives (such as "MySportsCenter"), are exploited (Fisher 2001).

With Disney reporting net income of $63 million for the three months ending December 31, 2000, down 77 percent from the same period a year before, some industry watchers have said Disney has been too hesitant in pursuing acquisitions, which will leave it a niche player in the entertainment industry (Gentile 2001). Amid speculation that Disney would pursue Yahoo! in its quest to compete with AOL Time Warner, Eisner told Wall Street analysts in February 2001 that Disney will "pounce and pounce well" when opportunities arise, but it will not make acquisitions just to show that it can (Gentile 2001).

Other analysts wonder if decisions such as the release of films to video hamper rerelease of classic films. Some speculate that as Disney becomes more prevalent, it runs the risk of lowering quality as the company licenses its characters to thousands of products. Although susceptible to large-scale missteps that leave it open to criticism, Disney shows no signs of backing off from its vertical integration strategies that have enabled it to control the customer, provide better service, generate economies of operations, and create a financially lucrative media empire.

In healthcare, vertical integration commonly refers to the ability of one provider system to offer many levels and intensities of service to patients and healthcare consumers in geographically contiguous regions. Further, vertical integration in healthcare delivery has been extended to the provision of insurance coverage, as this is an integral part of the nation's healthcare system.

As in other industries, healthcare organizations were initially drawn to vertical integration because of its potential economic benefits. And, like many companies outside of healthcare delivery, some degree of vertical integration is present in all but the smallest healthcare organizations. Economies from backwards integration have been pursued through support services such as laundry, billing, and malpractice insurance, although of late, many of these services have been increasingly viewed as candidates for outsourcing. The greatest economic benefits appear to emerge from forward vertical integration through control over medical referral patterns, although these benefits have proven far more elusive to realize than anticipated, despite massive efforts by healthcare organizations.

Still, the rationale for vertical integration in healthcare is compelling, according to Brown and McCool (1986), who cite four environmental factors to support this position.

1. *The nature of disease in populations*. Primary care requires a small base, but progressively larger populations are needed to support secondary and tertiary services; referral relationships among these levels of care should be enhanced by integration.
2. *Quality of care*. Subspecialty services are often materially better when sufficient patient volumes exist.
3. *Efficiency*. A comprehensive system has the potential to service a large volume of patients, thus minimizing unit cost.
4. *Image*. A well-functioning system of care is inherently appealing.

More recently, managed care growth and increased financial risk assumption by providers have created additional incentives to control costs, gain better and greater access to patient populations, and derive some financial benefit from the risk premium historically received by insurers.

As healthcare organizations weigh the advantages and risks of vertical integration, Harrigan (1984) suggests five dimensions of the vertical control continuum that should be kept in mind.

1. The breadth of the integration, such as the range of diagnosis-related groups (DRGs) cared for by the vertically integrated system
2. The degree of within-firm purchases and internal sales of vertically related services, as contrasted with the use of external sources ("outsourcing") for inputs and sales to other firms of one's service outputs
3. The number of stages in the vertically related value chain integrated or explicitly coordinated by a single organization, such as the health maintenance organization (HMO) that provides a wellness program, ambulatory care, acute inpatient care, long-term care, and home health care, as well as the full continuum of primary and specialty care that would be integrated at many stages in the value chain
4. The form of integration, that is, the nature of the coordination or ownership arrangements that link related services
5. The potential integration of health insurance with health services delivery

In the mid-1990s, vertical integration in healthcare delivery escalated in response to two factors: the oversupply of providers of nearly all types and changes in reimbursement. Oversupply has forced providers to seek closer relationships with referral sources to increase the likelihood of being able to maintain or increase utilization levels and revenue. Vertical integration was initially given a boost by the proposals for healthcare reform developed early in the Clinton administration, although none were enacted, and then by managed care growth and the emergence of risk-bearing contractual arrangements. According to a 1994 report by the Advisory Board Company, experts were touting capitation as the likely dominant reimbursement system of the near future. History has proven otherwise as capitation is now waning, as is vertical integration in healthcare delivery.

At the height of the recent vertical integration craze, the Advisory Board Company (1997) reported more than a 100 percent increase in the number of vertically integrated delivery systems between 1994 and 1996. Although reliable data are difficult to obtain, healthcare organizations with a significant degree of vertical integration today number in the thousands.

Nonetheless, many of the largest healthcare organizations in the United States are using vertical integration as a prominent competitive strategy. While environmental conditions continue to change and the theoretical benefits of vertical integration in healthcare delivery have been difficult to realize, few organizations have abandoned vertical integration, but have instead restructured, eliminated, or downsized some of their underperforming units. Although a restructuring phase as a prelude to the next phase of growth is not unusual after a period of rapid growth, it is unclear at this time how much of future development in healthcare delivery will be vertical in nature or if this competitive strategy is slowly being abandoned in favor of more promising alternatives.

The case studies that follow provide diverse perspectives on vertical integration in healthcare delivery and illustrate how this strategy is applied and the nature of its competitive benefits.

## Henry Ford Health System

Henry Ford Health System, located throughout southeastern Michigan, is considered one of the pioneer organizations in establishing a massive, vertically integrated nonprofit healthcare system that integrates primary and specialty care with research and education.

In 1915 automaker Henry Ford founded and financed the Henry Ford Hospital that today has grown into one of the nation's largest healthcare systems with 12 owned or affiliated hospitals and more than 25 ambulatory care centers and other health-related entities (Hoovers.com 2001b). The system is frequently cited as one of the nation's best healthcare providers. The 2000 annual ranking of hospitals by *U.S. News & World Report* ranked Henry Ford among the best hospitals in 12 of 17 specialty areas (Henry Ford Health System 2001a).

The original facilities included a private patient building for 48 patients, a surgical pavilion, research quarters, kitchens, laundry facilities, and a power plant. Henry Ford organized a staff of physicians and surgeons, many of whom came from Johns Hopkins (Henry Ford Health System Library 1998).

In 1925, the Henry Ford Hospital School of Nursing and a 300-room dormitory for nursing students were opened. The Edsel B. Ford Institute for Medical Research became the hospital's formal research division in 1947 (Henry Ford Health System Library 1998).

In 1975, as the demographics of Detroit and its patient base were changing, the hospital opened two large satellite centers with family and pediatric care, dentistry, behavioral health services, radiology, and pharmacy services, beginning the expansion of Henry Ford' services into the Detroit metropolitan area. Within the next ten years, five other suburban centers were opened, including a specialty center for treatment of chemical and alcohol dependency (Henry Ford Health System Library 1998).

During the late 1980s, the hospital affiliated with Cottage, Wyandotte, and Kingswood Hospitals and formed an HMO. In 1990, the Henry Ford Health System was established to oversee the hospitals, 25 suburban centers, and HMO (Henry Ford Health System Library 1998).

The Henry Ford Hospital is now a 903-bed tertiary care hospital, education, and research complex in Detroit. The hospital is a multiorgan transplantation center and Level 1 trauma center that is distinguished by its innovative patient-focused care systems, which organize care so that routine hospital services are provided by cross-trained teams of caregivers.

The Henry Ford Medical Group is one of the nation's largest and oldest group practices with 800 physicians in 40 specialties. The Henry Ford Health System is also affiliated with 1,800 private practice physicians (Henry Ford Health System 2001b). More than 2.5 million patient visits are recorded by the system annually and more than 30,000 outpatient surgery procedures are performed each year. The system's Health Alliance Plan now provides managed care and health insurance to more than 3,500 employers and 500,000 members as a wholly owned, nonprofit subsidiary of Henry Ford Health System. The system recorded $1.9 billion in revenues in 2000, with $60 million in uncompensated care. The system, governed by a 46-member board of community leaders, ranks as Michigan's sixth largest employer, with more than 16,000 full-time equivalent employees.

Henry Ford Health System has an expansive network of community services. Henry Ford at Home includes a medical supply retailer, Henry Ford Hospice (serving more than 1,100 patients annually), a Medicare-certified home health care agency, and three retail pharmacies. The system also has an autologous blood transfusion service, home infusion services, dialysis service in a three-state area, an emergency alert system, and a private-duty nursing service. Henry Ford also operates an innovative multidisciplinary center for seniors (Center for Senior Independence) and two nursing homes. In addition, the William Clay Ford Center for Athletic Medicine is a state-of-the-art facility for professional and amateur athletes, which also runs a fitness center for the system's employees (Henry Ford Health System 2001c).

Henry Ford has distinguished itself as a cutting-edge healthcare provider. More than $40 million is spent each year on medical research, ranking Henry Ford among the top 6 percent of all institutions receiving funding from the National Institutes of Health. The system is considered a leading research institution for headaches, strokes, heart conditions, cancer, and bone and joint diseases, with more than 1,000 research studies currently underway (Henry Ford Health System 2001c).

### Thriving as a Vertically Integrated System

Henry Ford Health System's commitment to fulfilling the promises of integrated delivery systems, particularly vertically integrated ones, is demonstrated by its establishment of the Center for Health System Studies. Originally established as a center for applied health services research, the center developed a strong focus on vertical integration issues in healthcare as the Henry Ford System evolved into a vertically organized organization. The center's current goals are to conduct research and ultimately improve the process of healthcare delivery, particularly integrated health systems and relationships among providers and levels of care that promote integration of patient care processes. Henry Ford Health System provides core funding for the center, which employs about 30 researchers and support staff. More than two-thirds of the center's budget is provided by external grants and contracts (Association for Health Services Research 1994).

Henry Ford Health System has thrived as a vertically integrated organization, but like other healthcare providers, particularly teaching hospitals, it has not staved off financial struggles. In 1995, citing anticipated cuts in Medicare and Medicaid and pressure from major employers, the system announced plans to cut operating costs by more than $150 million over three years, following the lead of one of its competitors, Detroit Medical Center, which earlier announced a $100 million cost-cutting initiative (Waldsmith 1995). Cost-cutting targets were achieved through cost reductions, particularly shorter hospital stays, and some revenue increases, such as increased enrollment in the Health Alliance Plan.

The March 27, 2000 issue of the *AHA News* cited Henry Ford Health System as one of the major teaching hospitals that is operating with a negative margin as a result of rising costs and falling revenue. (Costello 2000). For Henry Ford Health System, the financial struggles can be largely attributed to outside forces rather than poor strategy or execution. In 1999, the state of Michigan revamped its fee-for-service Medicaid program by requiring recipients to enroll in HMOs. The move cut the state's Medicaid costs by 25 percent but cost Henry Ford Health System $16 million in income. Balanced Budget Act cuts and slow payments from HMOs increased the system's losses to $40 million (Haugh 2000).

Henry Ford Health System has looked outside its organization for assistance when managing its own systems has detracted from its patient care focus. In January 2001, Henry Ford awarded a five-year, $82 million contract to Complete Business Solutions, Inc. (CBSI), a global technology services company. By outsourcing its IT applications, including application development, maintenance and support, and software projects, Henry Ford's Executive Vice President and Chief Operating Officer Nancy Schlichting, believes "The partnership with CBSI is an important step in allowing Henry Ford to direct all core resources to delivering the most personal, efficient, and effective health care to patients" (*Business Wire* 2001a). Outsourcing is also intended to help cut costs, saving about 3 to 5 percent for desktop support and 10 to 15 percent for telephone and data networking.

In addition to the contract with CBSI, Henry Ford turned over its IT operations to Siemens Enterprise Networks, LLC. The $100 million, five-year contract, also announced in January 2001, included the transition of about 100 Henry Ford IT employees to the Siemens payroll (*Business Wire* 2001b).

Industry watchers are predicting that massive and at times unwieldy vertically integrated systems like Henry Ford will continue to struggle financially, despite their demonstrated success in patient care, research, and education. Time will tell if Henry Ford can buck the downward financial spiral and continue its long history as a vertically integrated health system.

## Laurel Health System

Laurel Health System is a nonprofit health and human services organization that is widely considered one of the nation's best examples of a vertically integrated rural health system. Headquartered in Wellsboro in the northern tier of Pennsylvania, the system serves a rural population of about 50,000 located in four Pennsylvania counties and one New York county. Laurel Health System's affiliates work cohesively to provide a full range of services to this broad geographic region. One of the counties served by Laurel, Pennsylvania's Tioga County, is the second largest in land mass in the state but has one of the state's smallest population groups. Approximately 10 percent of Tioga's population lives below the poverty level (Zuckerman 1998).

Whereas Laurel Health System is now considered a role model for rural healthcare delivery, its history shows the many obstacles surmounted to create the system in 1989 and lay a foundation for later success. Because of the dispersed service area the system cares for, geographic barriers were reflected in the available healthcare services prior to formation of the system. The two population centers of the region each had separate healthcare services. Wellsboro had the region's only hospital, and Blossburg, 18 miles away, was the headquarters of North Penn Comprehensive Health Services, a network of health clinics and support services for a five-county area.

The 103-bed hospital, Soldiers + Sailors Memorial Hospital, had been a prosperous facility with strong community support since its founding during World War II. But by the early 1980s the hospital was struggling with the challenges facing most free-standing rural hospitals: changing reimbursement incentives, fluctuating utilization patterns, and increased competition. Hospital admissions dropped 23.5 percent from 1983 to 1985, and occupancy rates fell to 49.6 percent in 1985 (Zuckerman 1998).

The hospital was fortunate to have a strong reputation for quality care and a younger-than-average medical staff, but future performance was threatened. The hospital facility was aging and not well suited to the movement toward care being provided on an outpatient basis. While financially stable, 70 percent of its inpatients were covered by Medicare, Medicaid, or both, with compensation for these patients well below the cost of care (Zuckerman 1998). Most hospital admissions were also generated by medical staff members who were unaffiliated with the hospital. Although Soldiers + Sailors Memorial Hospital was the sole acute care provider in Tioga County, two major providers in counties close to the hospital's service area were moving into the county and affiliating with existing physician practices.

Fully aware that its vision of remaining an independent and locally controlled institution was threatened, Soldiers + Sailors Memorial Hospital initiated strategic and facility planning in 1987. Fundamental changes were agreed on such as meeting the non-acute needs of the region, improving the physical plant, linking existing and new group practices to the hospital, and networking with other providers. But the key element of the new direction was to place the hospital at the center of a vertically integrated regional healthcare system.

### Building a Vertically Integrated System

The starting point for building this new system was to affiliate with the North Penn Comprehensive Health Services to vertically integrate ambulatory and nonacute services. North Penn was already providing many of the services that were logical extensions of Soldiers + Sailors' mostly acute care presence: primary care health centers, mental health programs, home health services, non-medical elderly services, a Head Start program, and a residential program for troubled youth. The distribution of North Penn's healthcare centers would create a feeder system for the hospital through a hub-and-spoke model of care. With its unstable base of financial support (federal funding, private grants, sliding fees, and discounted payments) and fearing susceptibility to takeover by nonlocal groups, North Penn was willing to pursue affiliation discussions with the hospital.

Aware that affiliation would help both organizations retain local control and stave off competition, and fearful that delaying networking activities would make North Penn and the hospital vulnerable to closure or takeover, they agreed in theory that a new system could provide a seamless array of health and human services and take a proactive stance toward community health education and prevention. The formal decision to align did not come without some misgivings. North Penn and Soldiers + Sailors Memorial Hospital had a history of remaining separate for 15 years. North Penn was founded to provide local medical care when the hospital in Blossburg closed in 1973. Much of the blame for the hospital's failure was directed toward the Wellsboro community and its hospital, which had encouraged all of its physicians to practice only in Wellsboro (Zuckerman 1998).

The organizations proceeded slowly, first agreeing in 1988 to a letter of intent to collaborate. They then agreed to a three-year contract under which the hospital would manage North Penn and both parties would be able to evaluate organizational fit (Zuckerman 1998). In 1989, the affiliation was formalized with the creation of Laurel Health System to oversee the hospital, North Penn, and their affiliates.

In the 12 years since the founding of the system, Laurel Health System has moved purposefully toward fulfilling its promise to improve community health through education, prevention, and access to community health within a vertically integrated system of care. In addition to the hospital and North Penn, the system includes (Laurel Health System 2001):

- The Green Home—a skilled and intermediate nursing care facility with rehabilitation services
- Laurel Personal Care Home and the Laurels—an assisted-living complex
- Laurel Management Services—an inhouse group of staff consultants for system affiliates
- Laurel Realty—a not-for-profit holding company that owns and manages rental properties
- Soldiers + Sailors Memorial Service Volunteers—a coordinating group to organize auxiliary, volunteer, and fundraising activities

An impressive array of services is now provided by the system: 13 Head Start programs that also offer screening and medical examinations, community living programs at two sites for persons with developmental disabilities, a toll-free phone number and online information and referral service, inpatient and outpatient behavioral health programs, six primary care health centers, 12 senior centers and associated in-home services for the elderly, home health and hospice services, two wellness centers, diagnostic and residential treatment services for youth, foster care programs, occupational health services, a mobile community outreach program with educational and screening services, an alternative healing program, and a hospital with a full complement of inpatient and outpatient services (Laurel Health System 2001).

Changes have been made to continually adapt the system. In 1997, the six system affiliates, each of which had its own board, agreed to create one unified board of directors to oversee system operations (Laurel Health System 2001). Services have also been restructured and integrated through seven new management components intended to make services more cost-effective and efficient for area residents. Last, strong community support and involvement have helped the system identify unmet community needs and capitalize on the community spirit that takes great pride in having a locally owned and controlled network of health and human services that are so often fragmented in rural areas.

## CONCLUSION

Vertical integration is a conceptually appealing strategy that promises many benefits, but has rarely delivered them in healthcare or in other industries. Although the competitive advantages of vertical integration are numerous and compelling, not the least of which is to internalize the sales function and limit the need to compete externally in the market, the inability of nearly all organizations to realize them, even some of the largest and most admired companies in the United States and worldwide, is cause for some serious reflection.

Because vertical integration is such a theoretically appealing strategy, it will undoubtedly continue to have its proponents, and perhaps with time and additional experimentation, implementation principles for success will emerge. In the meantime, vertical integration remains a high-risk and high-reward strategy that few healthcare organizations should pursue.

# REFERENCES

Adalian, J. 1999. "ABC Gets Goose from Mouse." [Online article retrieval 11/6/200]. http:/www.findarticles.com/cf_0/m1312/11_375/55410437/p1/article.jhtml.

The Advisory Board Company. 1994. *Capitation I—The New American Medicine.* Washington, DC: The Advisory Board Company.

————. 1997. *American Healthcare 1997 State of the Union.* Washington, DC: The Advisory Board Company.

Allen, R. E. 1996. "When the Whole Becomes Less than the Sum of Its Parts: The Story Behind the AT&T Breakup." [Online retrieval 4/27/2000]. www.att.com/speeches/96/961101.raa.html.

Association for Health Services Research. 1994. "Henry Ford Health System Center for Health System Studies." [Online article retrieval 2/28/01]. www.ashr.org/publications/hsr_reports/1994/henry.htm.

AT&T. 2000a. "AT&T to Create Family of Four New Companies; Company to Offer to Exchange AT&T Common Stock for AT&T Wireless Stock." [Online retrieval 11/3/2000]. www.att.com/press/item/0,1354,3420,00.html.

————. 2000b. "Post Divestiture AT&T." [Online retrieval 11/3/2000]. www.att.com/history/history4.html.

Brown, M. and B. P. McCool. 1986. "Vertical Integration: Exploration of a Popular Strategic Concept." *Health Care Management Review* 11 (4): 67–79.

*Business Wire.* 2001a. "Henry Ford Health System and CBSI Ink Five-Year Outsourcing Agreement." *Business Wire,* January 22.

————. 2001b. "Siemens and Henry Ford Health System Expand Their Existing Outsourcing Agreement with $100 Million Contract over 5 Years." *Business Wire,* January 22.

Center for Media Education. September 25, 1995. "Public Interest Coalition Challenges Disney/ABC Merger." [Online press release retrieval 11/6/2000]. www.cni.org/Hforums/roundtable/1995-03/0185.html.

Communications Media Center at New York Law School. 1998. "Children's Broadcasting Corp. Wins Law Suit Against ABC and Disney." [Online article retrieval 11/6/2000]. www.cmcnyls.edu/public/Bulletins/Cbcwlabc.HTM.

Conrad, D. A. and W. L. Dowling. 1990. "Vertical Integration in Health Services: Theory and Managerial Implications." *Health Care Management Review* 15 (4): 83.

Costello, M. A. 2000. "Big Teaching Hospitals Feel Financial Pinch Especially Hard, MedPac Says." *AHA News*. [Online article retrieval 2/26/01]. www.healthforum.com/hfpubs/asp/Article Display.

*Disney 1998 Annual Report.* 1999. [Online retrieval 11/6/200]. http://disney.go.com/corporate/investors/financial/annual.html.

Eisner, M. 2000. Speech to Shareholders [Online retrieval 2/23/00]. http://disney.com/investors/events/2000mtgeisner.html.

Fairness and Accuracy in Reporting (FAIR). 2000. "The Walt Disney Company." [Online article retrieval 11/6/2000]. http://www.fair.org/media outlets/disney-info.html.

————. December 1995. "Hightower Gets the Mickey Mouse Treatment." [Online article retrieval 11/6/2000]. http://www.fair.org/extra/9512/hightower.html.

Fisher, M. 2001. "Disney Puts a Stop to Go.com." [Online article retrieval 11/6/2000]. www.localbusiness.com/Story/0,1118,NOCITY_600566,00.html.

Gentile, G. 2001. "Disney Chairman Interested in Yahoo!." [Online article retrieval 2/7/2001]. http://news.excite.com/news/ap/010207/earns-disney.

Harrigan, K. R. 1984. "Formulating Vertical Integration Strategies." *Academy of Management Review* 9: 638–52, in Conrad and Dowling, op cit., 83–84.

Haugh, R. 2000. "The Ratings Slide." *Hospitals & Health Networks*. [Online article retrieval 2/26/01]. www.healthforum.com/hfpubs/asp/Article Display.

Henry Ford Health System. 2001a. "Henry Ford Ranked for Excellence." [Online article retrieval 2/8/2001]. www.henryfordhealth.org/body.cfm?id=33666&ref=224&action=detail.

————. 2001b. "Henry Ford Medical Group is One of the Nation's Largest and Oldest Practices." [Online article retrieval 2/8/2001]. www.henryfordhealth.org/body.cfm?id=37839.

————. 2001c. "Community Care Services." [Online article retrieval 2/8/2001]. www.henryfordhealth.org/body.cfm?id=36955.

Henry Ford Health System Library. 1998. "Henry Ford Health System History." [Online article retrieval 2/28/2001]. http://sladen.hfhs.org/library/archives/hfhs-history.htm.

Hoovers.com. 2001a. "The Walt Disney Company." [Online article retrieval 2/7/01]. www.hoovers.com/co/capsule/3/0,2163,11603,00.html.

————. 2001b. "Henry Ford Health System." [Online article retrieval 2/8/01]. www.hoovers.com/co/capsule/1/0,2163,44861,00.html.

Laurel Health System. 2001. [Online retrieval 3/5/01]. www.laurelhs.org.

McChesney, R. W. 1997. "The Global Media Giants." [Online article retrieval 11/6/2000]. http://www.fair.org/extra9711/gmg.html.

Meyerson, B. 2000. "AT&T to Break into Smaller Companies." [Online article retrieval 10/25/2000]. www.excite.com/news/ap/001025/08/att.

Porter, M. E. 1980. *Competitive Strategy: Techniques for Analyzing Industries and Competitors*. New York: The Free Press, a division of Macmillan, Inc.

Reuters Company News. 2001. "Disney Won't See Double Digit '01 Earnings Growth." [Online article retrieval 2/7/01]. www.hoovershbn.hoovers.com/bi...:eob9.

Stone, A. 1993. "Organization Theory and the Walt Disney Company." [Online retrieval 4/27/2000]. http://socrates.berkely.edu:4050/ids-org.html.

Waldsmith, L. 1995. "Henry Ford Health System to Cut $150 Million in Costs." *Detroit News,* August 23, 1995.

Wallace, B. 2000. "The Next Frontier." [Online article retrieval 3/9/2000]. www.informationweek.com/774/carrier/html.

Zuckerman, A. M. 1998. *Ambulatory Care in Integrated Delivery Systems*. Chicago: American Hospital Publishing, Inc.

# CHAPTER 3

# Horizontal Integration

## INTRODUCTION

HORIZONTAL INTEGRATION HAS become a common strategy for gaining increased market power and cost savings. In the healthcare sector, horizontal integration appeared first among for-profit providers; most recently, it has emerged by way of mergers and acquisitions among both for-profit and nonprofit healthcare organizations, often through transactions that are becoming increasingly larger.

This chapter presents a discussion of horizontal integration, including case studies and information on its competitive advantages and when it is best not to apply horizontal integration.

## HORIZONTAL INTEGRATION DEFINED

Horizontal integration is the combination of similar businesses or business units into one coordinated enterprise. In healthcare, the merger of hospitals with each other and of two or more physician practices, home care agencies, and the like was a common phenomenon in the mid- to late 1990s. While the number of mergers and acquisitions in the hospital sector has dropped recently, with 86 transactions noted in 2000, versus 110 in 1999 and 197 deals in 1997, the transactions are becoming larger. The largest merger and acquisition in the hospital sector in 2000 was four times larger than the largest one in 1999 (Irving Levin Associates 2001).

Until the 1990s, most horizontal integration in healthcare delivery, especially in the not-for-profit sector, was through internal growth and expansion. While internally generated growth still occurs, the more common approach today is to achieve growth in a particular area of business through merger or acquisition that may be achieved in a specific market or across markets in regional or multistate horizontal chains.

Horizontal integration can take many organizational forms, with varying degrees of interdependence as illustrated in Figure 3.1. Most typical are mergers or acquisitions, although joint ventures, joint operating arrangements, contracts and subcontracts, and shared service organizations are other vehicles that have been used by healthcare organizations to bring together similar enterprises into one that has a single purpose and common direction and operation.

## HORIZONTAL INTEGRATION AS A COMPETITIVE ADVANTAGE

Horizontal integration generally is used as a strategy to increase market power. By combining multiple healthcare enterprises into one organization, market share and total revenues usually increase as a result of being the sole or dominant provider in a region (Weil 2000). Other competitive benefits may be realized including greater market presence as more contacts with patients and greater visibility lead to a higher profile and image and, ideally, more business.

Clinical synergies may also emerge as complementary clinical capabilities of collaborating organizations result in cross-referrals or development of new or expanded capabilities that neither may

**Figure 3.1: Range of Horizontal Integration Options**

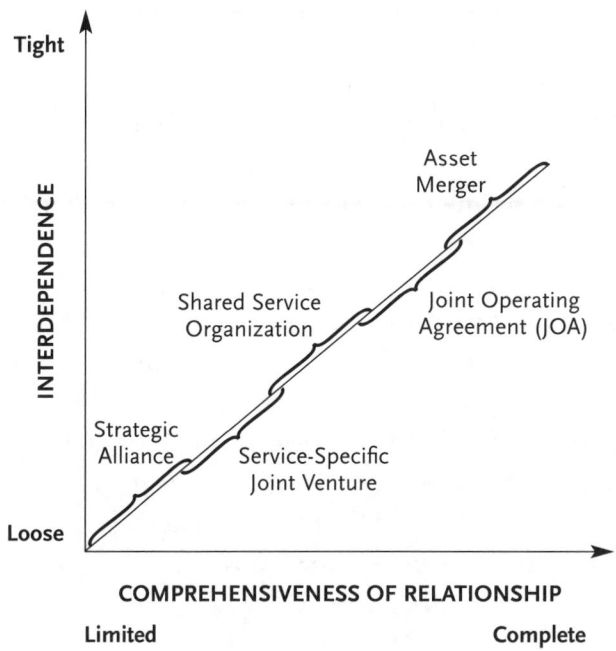

*Source:* Reprinted with permission from Health Strategies & Solutions, Inc., © 2001.

have the resources to develop on their own. Leverage with buyers from a concentration of market power may allow the healthcare organization to charge higher prices and provide services on more favorable terms to the seller. Government regulators have attempted to use their antitrust enforcement powers to prevent noncompetitive markets from forming (Lutz 1996) because of the potential for increased prices and reduced consumer welfare.

Lower costs are another main competitive advantage that may result from horizontal integration. Economies of scale (e.g., better rates or terms from suppliers) and elimination of duplicative services should generate operational efficiencies and ultimately cost savings (Lynk 1995). Reduction of unused capacity through pooled staffing and improved management and production processes may also occur (Connor et al. 1997). Clearly, reduced costs, all other things being equal, can materially enhance the competitive advantage of a healthcare organization or any other enterprise.

While the theoretical benefits of horizontal integration appear clear on paper, realizing these competitive advantages has proved elusive for many organizations. First, consider the cost of the merger, including the costs of linking or replacing information systems, severance costs, and the often hidden cost of distracting the organization from other pressing business demands (Trespacz 1999). Other industry experts warn about the volatility of today's markets. Bernard Ferrari, M.D., J.D., of McKinsey & Co. points out: "If you are aggregating or consolidating to play an old game, and the game changes to where the aggregation has no value, you've just spent a lot of money for nothing" (Trespacz 1999).

Some key issues to consider as horizontally integrated organizations come together include the following (Trespacz 1999):

- Move quickly to keep the best people.
- Clarify who will be making decisions and when.
- Establish a new vision for the company, including what value will be added by the mergers.
- Pay close attention to organizational cultures, striving to be inclusive when possible.
- Seek savings first in areas that are nondisruptive to the core business, such as purchasing and supply management.

Horizontal integration is a common competitive strategy outside of healthcare delivery, with the potential for increased market power, cost savings, and higher stock prices often cited as the driving forces. In 1998, the worldwide value of mergers and acquisitions reached almost $2.5 trillion—50 percent higher than in 1997 (Viscio et al. 1999), with much of this activity considered horizontal in nature.

## HORIZONTAL INTEGRATION CASE STUDIES

Horizontal integration in recent years has been especially prevalent in the banking, telecommunications, and automotive industries, as well as in healthcare insurance and pharmaceuticals. A few examples illustrate the potential outcomes of this strategy.

### Aetna and U.S. Healthcare

The $8.9 billion merger of Aetna Insurance Company and U.S. Healthcare in 1996 created the largest healthcare insurer in the country, providing coverage to 23 million people or 1 in every 12 Americans (Aetna, Inc., 1996). The new company, with a presence in all 50 states, set the goals of providing quality healthcare services at a reasonable cost on a national scale, meeting the needs of consumers and employers large and small, and generating significant growth opportunities as the dominant player in managed healthcare (Aetna, Inc. 1996).

With Aetna already considered one of the leading healthcare insurance companies with particular expertise in managing large, multisite insurance plans and U.S. Healthcare recognized as a top HMO company with high rankings for customer satisfaction, hopes were high that the merger was an enviable strategic fit that would lay the foundation for growth, innovation, and strong financial performance. The company was touted as having the scale and expertise to thrive in the dynamic healthcare market.

Synergies from the combined health businesses were expected to realize an additional $300 million after taxes within 18 months, generated primarily from additional HMO membership and cross-selling opportunities with specialty health and group life, as well as reductions in medical and operating expenses (Aetna, Inc. 1996).

Industry analysts questioned the wisdom of the merger from the start. Aetna, which had previously shunned the HMO model, pursued the U.S. Healthcare merger as HMOs were becoming less popular among consumers who were beginning to favor the less restrictive preferred provider organizations (PPOs). Aetna also did not stop with the U.S. Healthcare merger, but launched into a buying spree that added the healthcare insurance businesses of New York Life Insurance Company in 1998 and Prudential Insurance Company of America in 1999. By February 2000, Aetna's stock price fell to $40 from about $100 a year earlier, signaling that the company may have expanded too quickly to realize the anticipated benefits of the mergers.

*Failure to Meet Financial Goals*

Five years after the U.S. Healthcare merger, Aetna is mired in deep financial troubles with its chief financial officer resigning in April 2001 amid rumors that first-quarter earnings are significantly below expectations due to unexpectedly high medical costs from higher utilization of healthcare services in the fourth quarter of 2000. It is also reported that Aetna may fail to meet previous earnings forecasts for 2001 (Hoovers 2001a). Aetna's profit margin (2.5 percent) in 1999 was among the lowest in the managed care industry (Reuters Company News 2001) with 2000 losses posted at $127.1 million on revenue of $26.8 billion (Brubaker 2001).

*The "New" Aetna Under Fire*

Since late 2000 when Aetna moved to focus on its troubled healthcare business by selling off its financial services and international operations to a Dutch firm, high-level management changes have occurred including a new chairman, a new chief of health operations, and a new chief medical officer (Hoovers 2001a). The management changes have done little to stave off scathing criticism and lawsuits by doctors and patients and bitter disappointment that the "new" Aetna, formerly know as the stalwart "Mother Aetna," has become emblematic of everything that is wrong among healthcare insurers (Brubaker 2001). According to a *Washington Post* report, Aetna has become the "undisputed bully" of the managed care industry, known for dictating how much physicians should be paid and how they should treat their patients (Brubaker 2001). For example, Aetna pays $80 for a comprehensive cardiac consultation, which is less than half of what Medicare pays (Brubaker 2001).

Aetna also underestimated the value of its personnel to its formerly solid reputation. With the Aetna–U.S. Healthcare merger, many experienced employees were replaced by inexperienced newcomers who could handle only one-third to one-fourth the number of claims processed by their predecessors (Trespacz 1999). In 1997, Aetna took a $160 million charge for unanticipated medical costs; because it had lost so many customers, due in large part to poor customer service, it was unable to track what it was spending (Trespacz 1999).

In February 2001, the 7,000-member Connecticut State Medical Society filed a lawsuit against Hartford, Connecticut–based Aetna for unfair and deceptive practices (Brubaker 2001). Complaints that Aetna does not address patients' medical needs, pay their bills promptly, or answer patient questions have led to class action lawsuits. Aetna's executives now admit that "we bit off more than we could chew" in the rush to dominate the managed care industry and that Aetna had become "unbending and tough and hard in an attempt to control costs." Aetna leadership has also admitted to paying too much for U.S. Healthcare. Aetna's current worth is estimated at $5 billion, not quite half of what the company paid for U.S. Healthcare (Brubaker 2001).

Aetna's new management team has a long struggle ahead as it tries to salvage any of the competitive benefits of its horizontal integration strategies and restore its financial footing and damaged relationships with thousands of patients and physicians.

The field of financial services, and banking in particular, continues to consolidate into larger and larger entities that are some of the best illustrations of the benefits and pitfalls of horizontal integration. Amid the many examples of poorly performing horizontal combinations, one of the most successful and largest transactions to date has been the merger of Bank of America and NationsBank.

The combination of the two banking companies, the new Bank of America Corporation is considered the first truly national banking franchise in the United States with about 4,500 retail branches in 21 states (Hoovers 2001b). One in every three United States households banks with Bank of America (Bank of America 2001a). Its operations consist of three major businesses. Its Consumer and Commercial Bank currently has the number one market share in U.S. deposits, customer households, business customers, banking offices, and ATMs. Bank of America's Financial Services Bank includes principal investing and wealth management services. The third major business is the Global Corporate and Investment Bank, which is a dominant financial services provider in 37 countries (Infirmation Link Corporation 2001).

This banking conglomerate is the result of the $43 billion merger of NationsBank Corporation and Bank of America Corporation in September 1998. Remarks by NationsBank Vice Chairman and Chief Financial Officer James Hance at an April 1998 press conference included comments that the merger is "the best combination of markets, customers, product capabilities, delivery channels, marketing and technology prowess, and people to achieve huge earnings potential" (Bank of America 1998). He also noted that the new company would reach more customers more effectively, generate significant potential for productivity improvement and operating efficiencies by reducing overhead and redundant expenses across business lines, and create tremendous balance sheet strength (Bank of America 1998).

In 2000, Bank of America reported operating earnings of $7.86 billion on revenues of more than $33 billion (Bank of America 2001b). The company missed its annual financial goals for growth in revenue, net income, and earnings per share by significant margins. Bank of America cites several factors that have contributed to its financial shortfalls. Higher interest rates affected the company's earnings and stock. In addition, weakening credit quality among corporations offset gains in the firm's core businesses.

Bank of America also admits that the transformation of the new company following the merger has not been as rapid as initially projected, leading the company to reduce middle management positions, streamline the organization, move decision making closer to the customer, and free up funds for investment in growth opportunities.

### Solid Positioning for Future Success

Despite these setbacks, the company believes it is well positioned to withstand further slowdowns in the economy and credit quality declines, citing its $50 billion in capital and reserves and pretax operating income of over $3 billion per quarter. Bank of America also notes that its size, geographic reach, diverse loan portfolio, positive trends in customer service, and growth in key businesses will help the company fare well against competitors.

The company is also confident that it has a clear vision of what it wants to be and that the major components to realize the vision are in place. While there is evidence that its strategy is working, the challenge now is to make the company function as a unified whole or "digi-brick institution," a term coined by Bank of America, and not a disjointed collection of businesses. The company has also stated its commitment to continue to transform from a company that grows by acquisition to a customer-focused, internal growth company. To achieve this goal, Bank of America will shift its focus from merger transactions to improving customer service, reengineering work processes, and reinvesting cost savings into high-growth areas of the company.

According to retiring Bank of America Chairman and Chief Executive Officer Hugh McColl, the company is firm in its conviction that once the "dust settles and clouds lift, Bank of America will be the best financial services company in the country, with a stock price to match its fundamentally solid financial performance."

## HORIZONTAL INTEGRATION STRATEGY IN HEALTHCARE

Prior to the early 1990s, horizontal integration in healthcare delivery occurred infrequently, but it has become an increasingly prevalent event in healthcare delivery since then. While some not-for-profit multihospital systems had been formed and some large physician groups were also in existence in the 1970s and 1980s, the major evidence of horizontal integration was in the for-profit sector, principally among nursing home chains, but also in a few large hospital chains and select other businesses, such as dialysis. Hospital Corporation of America, Humana, and Beverly Enterprises were among the most visible examples of horizontal integration prior to the 1990s. All were formed and developed to capitalize on both the market-power and economies-of-scale aspects of horizontal integration and, judging from their performance at that time, succeeded admirably for awhile.

Horizontal integration more recently has been driven by the oversupply of providers of nearly all types that has led to a survival-of-the-fittest mentality. The grouping of like types of providers horizontally has essentially been a reaction to price pressures and, to a lesser degree, other external pressures such as government regulatory mandates, increasingly complex issues in insurance and health plan contracting, and more favorable treatment of larger entities in capital markets.

Horizontal integration has occurred principally as a defensive strategy. Much of the motivation and rationale driving the integration that has occurred is to generate economies and reduce costs so that organizations are positioned to better manage their financial prospects as increasing price pressures bear down on them. Coupled with this rationale and motivation is the belief that larger entities will provide more protection and ensure survival for some organizations that might not survive independently against the vagaries of the market.

Horizontal integration continues to be a valid and important strategy for many healthcare organizations today. With forecasts of continued yet slower consolidation of healthcare providers, horizontal integration is likely to be on the horizon for most providers, whether it is an explicit part of their strategy or not. And horizontal integration must deliver clear, measurable market-related benefits and cost benefits as noted above, or ultimately it will fail.

According to research by Weil (2000), for healthcare mergers to achieve their projected savings, leaders must be willing to more vigorously coordinate key clinical services to reduce competition for revenue among members of the new organization, close superfluous hospitals and centralize costly tertiary services, encourage surplus physicians to relocate to underserved areas, and provide direction to integrate the best of what the competitive and regulatory strategies are able to generate to improve access and quality of care, and reduce total health expenditures.

Research to date seems to indicate that the most successful horizontal mergers involve two medium-sized, high-case mix, not-for-profit hospitals in the same community. These organizations tend to increase market share, implement economies of scale, better control prices in their local market, and generate operational savings (Weil 2000).

### Reasons Horizontal Integration Fails

Horizontal integration may not be an appropriate strategy to pursue in a number of situations. Among the more frequent reasons why horizontal integration fails or should not be considered are:

- *Diseconomies of scale.* At a certain size, organizations are so large that costs per unit of service increase, rather than decrease, with added size. Considerable research was conducted in the 1960s and 1970s about whether economies of scale occurred in hospitals and at what size they were achieved. These studies were somewhat inconclusive in that they revealed that if economies of scale existed, hospital size had little influence on them (Yafchak 2000). More recent research reveals that since 1994 larger hospitals started showing some economies of scale; however, whatever enhanced financial performance results from the economies are offset by reductions in asset turnover that occur as size increases (Yafchak 2000). Nonetheless, diseconomies of scale appear to continue to plague some healthcare organizations. In addition, while organizations can use market share clout to get volume discounts from suppliers, once the organization gets past about 20 percent of any suppliers' business, there is the risk of bankrupting them by demanding lower unit prices (Trespacz 1999).

- *Market dominance.* In some markets, a healthcare provider is already dominant and further growth through horizontal combination in that market may cause antitrust scrutiny and, ultimately, be prohibited. The situations in which market dominance exists in healthcare used to be clearer, but recent court decisions have blurred the distinctions in this area and made them less apparent, perhaps eliminating obstacles that previously inhibited some horizontal affiliations. In addition, as of February 2001, hospitals will no longer have to file premerger notification with government antitrust regulators for joint venture deals and mergers worth less than $50 million. Prior to this change, the Federal Trade Commission had set the threshold for required notification on mergers and joint venture arrangements at $15 million (*AHA News* 2001).

- *Stakeholder opposition.* In some situations, board members, physicians, employees, and community leaders may be unalterably opposed to any combinations, often as a result of highly unsatisfactory prior experience, and successfully resist integration regardless of its merits.
- *Uniqueness.* Some organizations may provide a highly specialized service or have a monopoly in a region. Thus no horizontal integration opportunities exist. Organizations may also have such a unique culture that merging with any other organization is not feasible or advisable.

The following case studies clarify how the horizontal integration strategy is applied by healthcare providers and the nature of the competitive benefits these organization realize.

## Catholic Health Initiatives

Catholic Health Initiatives is currently the second largest Catholic healthcare system in the country (Hoovers 2001c), with about 75,000 employees and annual operating revenue of $6 billion (Catholic Health Initiatives 2001a). The system is currently composed of 68 hospitals and 49 long-term care, assisted-living facilities, and residential units located throughout 22 states (Catholic Health Initiatives 2001a). The system includes nonprofit and for-profit corporations and other organizations that own and operate healthcare facilities or provide healthcare services (Catholic Health Initiatives 2000). Although operating a number of healthcare businesses, the system is principally a horizontal combination formed to achieve benefits from the consolidation of similar enterprises.

The foundation of this system was formed in 1995 when a group of healthcare leaders started exploring approaches for preserving and strengthening the Catholic health ministry (Catholic Health Initiatives 2001a). Their vision was to create a national healthcare organization, governed by a religious-lay partnership and sponsored by multiple congregations, that would move healthcare delivery into horizontally integrated networks and create opportunities to promote healthy communities and new ministries by integrating healthcare with pastoral and social services.

In 1996, Catholic Health Initiatives was formed through the consolidation of Catholic Health Corporation of Omaha, Nebraska, Franciscan Health System, Aston, Pennsylvania, and the Sisters of Charity Health Care Systems, Cincinnati, Ohio. Later, Sisters of Charity of Nazareth Health System in Bardstown, Kentucky, became the tenth sponsoring congregation of religious women.

*Realizing the Benefits of Horizontal Integration*

Catholic Health Initiatives is committed to using its combined strength to create new models of healthcare that are forged through collaborative relationships and partnerships with community agencies and other healthcare organizations. The system's five regions claim to benefit from Catholic Health Initiatives' national presence and financial strength. Each region measures its accomplishments against others in the system and learns from best practices and shared experiences while benefiting from reduced costs gained through shared services, including information systems, purchasing, and insurance buying (Mercy Medical Center 2001).

In addition, the system's Mission and Ministry Fund uses its financial resources to improve the health of communities served by Catholic Health Initiatives facilities (Catholic Health Initiatives 2001a). For example, in October 1999, the system bought a $1 million certificate of deposit from the Louisville Community Development Bank, purchased through the system's Direct Community Investment fund. The funds are then made available as low-interest loans or other financial support to organizations that provide access to jobs, housing, food, education, and healthcare to low-income and minority groups (American City Business Journals, Inc. 1999). In 1999, the Direct Community Investment Fund gave more than $7 million to nonprofit organizations and projects that promote healthy communities (Catholic Health Initiatives 2001a).

The system appears to be performing well under volatile market conditions. Financial statements for the fiscal year ending June 30, 2000 reveal significant improvement over the prior year's performance due to improved operations, additional revenue generation, cost management, and stronger strategic focus. Net income for 2000 was $96.5 million compared to the net loss of $53.8 million in 1999, resulting in a positive financial turn of more than $150 million between the fiscal years (Catholic Health Initiatives 2000). Other key indicators of strong financial performance improvement from 1999 to 2000 include a 5.5 percent increase in patient services revenues, with a 15.6 percent increase in outpatient care net revenues as a result of an enhanced focus on ambulatory care services as a vital component of the system's ministry. Long-term care revenues grew 2.5 percent and home-based revenues rose 11.8 percent from 1999 to 2000. The system accepts and treats all patients regardless of the ability to pay and provided $148 million in charity care in 2000, an increase of $14 million over 1999 (Catholic Health Initiatives 2000).

### Ensuring Future Performance

With performance improvement initiatives underway at many of its facilities, Catholic Health Initiatives expects see to further financial improvement in 2001 (Catholic Health Initiatives 2000). The system will also continue to monitor its facilities to ensure a balance between community service and financial viability. In June 2000, Catholic Health Initiatives discontinued it health maintenance organizations, taking a loss of $18.6 million (Catholic Health Initiatives 2000).

Most recently, Catholic Health Initiatives and Catholic Health East signed a letter of intent in January 2001 to transfer five of Catholic Health Initiatives' greater Philadelphia–area hospitals and two long-term-care facilities to Catholic Health East, another major Catholic system (Catholic Health Initiatives 2001b). Reasons cited for the transfer were greater efficiencies and economies of scale to enhance financial and operational performance for the seven facilities. With Catholic Health East already holding a strong six-hospital presence in greater Philadelphia and southern New Jersey, both organizations felt the best interests of the communities would be served by a unified Catholic health system. Catholic Health Initiatives will, however, hold onto a hospital in Reading, Pennsylvania, and several other smaller healthcare facilities in the area (Catholic Health Initiatives 2001b).

While other horizontally integrated healthcare systems are struggling to realize the benefits touted during their formation, Catholic Health Initiatives seems to be remaining true to its mission of promoting healthy communities with a spirit of innovation and protecting its financial viability to ensure that its legacy continues to meet the needs of communities it serves. Its efforts have been acknowledged nationally, most recently by receiving the 2001 National Quality Health Care Award from the National Committee for Quality Health Care.

### Beverly Enterprises, Inc.

Beverly Enterprises, Inc., headquartered in Fort Smith, Arkansas, is one of the leading nursing home operators in the United States with 560 facilities in 30 states (Hoovers 2001d). Beverly also operates assisted-living centers, outpatient therapy clinics, hospice programs, and home health care centers. As with other companies that invested heavily in long-term care, the firm has been hit hard by declining government reimbursement, forcing intense focus on controlling rising healthcare costs as Medicare continues to squeeze profit margins. With the restoration of some Medicare funding cuts, possibly resulting in an additional $20 million in revenues for Beverly in 2000 and $30 million in 2001, the firm has had a respite recently from the siege it has faced from regulators (*Arkansas Democrat* 2001).

The company is organized into two operating segments. Beverly Healthcare oversees operations of the nursing facilities and assisted-living centers. Beverly Care Alliance operates the outpatient therapy clinics, home care centers, and hospice programs.

Beverly began as a one-facility operation in 1963 and went public in 1966. Starting in the early 1970s, the company began to acquire additional nursing homes to strengthen its financial and operating base. Beverly's first major acquisition that set the stage for becoming a key player in the industry was a chain of nursing homes based in Arkansas. These facilities doubled Beverly's size, making it the number two company in the long-term-care field (Beverly Enterprises 2001a).

The company continued its expansion, eventually emerging as a horizontally integrated organization offering services throughout the post–acute care continuum. A few of the services provided through Beverly's extensive network include cancer care and chemotherapy, diabetes care, joint replacement, intravenous therapies, wound management, postoperative recovery, ventilator care and weaning, dialysis services, and hospice care. Services are provided at Beverly facilities and in partnership with existing providers, where services are tailored to meet local demand and payment constraints.

Financially, Beverly has exhibited variable and at times rocky performance during volatile periods, such as 1999 when an estimated 10 to 12 percent of nursing home beds in the United States were operated by bankrupt providers, including several leading national chains (Beverly Enterprises 2000). Beverly also notes that market capitalization of long-term-care companies dropped from $25 billion in 1997 to $6 billion in 2000.

Following 1999's poor performance, the company took action to strengthen its competitive position: streamlining operations, reengineering key support functions, and emphasizing greater personal and organizational accountability. Beverly also converted excess capacity in 29 facilities to meet the growing demand for care of Alzheimer patients.

William Floyd, Beverly's chief executive officer since January 2001, states that "Beverly is in a position of relative financial strength and stability today, in an industry where most major companies are bankrupt" (*Business Wire* 2001). Floyd also contends that the company is building on its financial and operating strengths and is gaining significant momentum in achieving gains in all of Beverly's businesses (*Business Wire* 2001). Floyd predicts that improved operating effectiveness and cost control measures should enable Beverly to increase operating earnings by at least 10 percent in 2001.

For the fiscal year ending December 31, 2000, revenues rose 3 percent to $2.63 billion, while its net loss fell 60 percent to $54.5 million. Revenues reflect an increase in service rates and acquisitions, while the lower loss is tied to fewer legal settlements from federal government investigations (Yahoo! Finance Market Guide 2001). Preliminary operating results for the first quarter of 2001 are on target and should equal or slightly exceed the six cents per share earned in the first quarter of 2000 (BW HealthWire 2001).

### Legal Disputes at Odds with Vision

Despite its financial recovery, Beverly has been plagued by ongoing disputes with the Occupational Safety and Health Administration and the National Labor Relations Board, as well as numerous lawsuits nationwide. In February 2000, Beverly was ordered to pay $175 million and sell ten facilities as part of a Medicare fraud settlement. Another major Medicare fraud settlement was reached in August 1999 (Elderweb 2001).

In January 1997, Beverly Enterprises was ordered to reinstate hundreds of workers represented by the Service Employees International Union, based on an injunction sought by the National Labor Relations Board. The strike had lasted only three days when Beverly responded by permanently replacing all strikers and denying other workers their previous positions (American City Business Journals, Inc. 1997). In June 1996, two large labor unions asked Florida Governor Lawton Chiles to stop the firm from expanding in Florida, alleging unsafe patient conditions at existing Beverly facilities (American City Business Journals, Inc. 1996). The high-profile legal wranglings seem to be at odds with Beverly's vision "to be the most respected, successful and desired provider of healthcare services in the communities we serve" (Beverly Enterprises 2000).

### Growth Plan

Recent Beverly initiatives include the renaming of its rehabilitation company, which was spun off as a separate operating unit of Beverly more than two years ago. The new name, Aegis Therapies, is part of Beverly's strategic growth plan designed to increase market share. Since its spin-off, Aegis has grown and developed innovative projects such as its partnership with Nautilus Human Performance Systems to outfit nursing homes with strength training equipment (BridgeNews 2001).

With sharp increases in patient care liability costs in Florida and the possible influence of negative media coverage, Beverly has been exploring the potential sale of its Florida facilities, which could result in a reported loss for the company, with proceeds from the sale used primarily to reduce debt. This move fits within Beverly's three-year strategic growth plan that calls for streamlining its portfolio of nursing homes to strengthen its financial position. The initiative is based on analyses that demonstrated that 80 percent of Beverly's total operating profits were generated by roughly 40 percent of its nursing homes. The growth plan also calls for stepping up internal growth of Beverly's existing businesses with the goal of having these operations generate one-third of company revenues (Beverly Enterprises 2001b). Both of these moves may signal that Beverly is phasing out its massive merger and acquisition strategy in favor of leaner, more manageable operations that still remain true to the competitive advantages of horizontal integration.

## CONCLUSION

Horizontal integration has enjoyed a modest amount of success among healthcare providers and in other industries; however, many organizations, and healthcare organizations in particular, have not achieved the benefits in market leverage or cost savings that appeared to be obtainable prior to integration, and only a minority of organizations have gained true competitive advantage from this strategy. Furthermore, as a competitive strategy, the inability of all but a few to develop meaningful, synergistic linkages across business units or product lines in horizontally combined organizations renders this strategy a failure in healthcare to date. Although pursuit of appropriate horizontal integration still seems to be a valid course for today's market conditions, in the absence of much more successful execution of the strategy, it appears to be inefficient, except in unusual circumstances in which extreme dominance is gained or huge cost advantages are realized.

## REFERENCES

AHA News. 2001. "Change to Federal Law Exempts Smaller Mergers from Antitrust Filing." [Online article retrieval 5/2/2001]. http://www.ahanews. com/asp/NewsNowDisplay.asp?PubID=2&ArticleID=144&Keyword=an.

Aetna, Inc. 1996. "Aetna and U.S. Health Care Agree to Merge." [Online article retrieval 3/12/01]. http://www.aetna.com/news/1996/pr_19960401a.htm.

American City Business Journals, Inc. 1996. "Union Targets Nursing Home Giant Beverly Enterprises." [Online article retrieval 4/23/01]. http://orlando.bcentral.com/orlando/stories/1996/06/24/newscolumn3.html.

———. 1997. "Beverly Enterprises Must Rehire Striking Workers." [Online article retrieval 4/23/01]. http://Pittsburgh.bcentral.com/pittsburgh/stories/1997/01/20/daily17.html.

———. 1999. "Catholic Health Initiatives Invests in Development Bank." [Online article retrieval 4/17/01]. http://louisville.bcentral.com/louisville/stories/1999/10/18/daily4.html.

*Arkansas Democrat.* 2001. "Chief Financial Officer of Smith, Ark., Health Care Firm Resigns." [Online article retrieval 4/23/01]. www.ardemgaz.com.

Bank of America. 1998. Remarks at the BankAmerica/NationsBank Merger Press Conference. [Online article retrieval 3/13/01]. www.bankofamerica.com/newsroom/speech.cfm?SpeechID=speech.19980413.01.htm.

———. 2001a. "50 Fast Facts about Bank of America." [Online article retrieval 4/17/01]. www.bankofamerica.com/facts/index.cfm?Menu_Sel=fast facts.

———. 2001b. "2000 Summary Annual Report." [Online retrieval 4/17/01]. www.bankofamerica.com/annualreport/ceo_letter.cfm.

Beverly Enterprises. 2000. "1999 Annual Report." [Online retrieval 4/23/01]. www.beverlynet.com.

———. 2001a. "Background and History." [Online article retrieval 4/23/01]. http://www.beverlynet.com/profile/history/co200.html.

———. 2001b. "Strategic Growth Plan." [Online retrieval 4/23/01]. http://beverlynet.com/investor/articles/in400.html.

BridgeNews. 2001. "Beverly Rehabilitation Changes Name to AEGIS Therapies." [Online article retrieval 4/23/01]. http://hoovnews.com/fp.asp?layout=displaynews&doc/id=NR20010404260.4173.

*Business Wire.* 2001. "Floyd Appointed CEO of Beverly Enterprises." [Online article retrieval 3/13/2001]. www.hoovers.com.

Brubaker, B. 2001. "Aetna's Unmet Claims." *Washington Post,* February 25, F1.

BW Healthwire. 2001. "Beverly Previews On-Target First Quarter Operating Earnings." [Online article retrieval 4/23/01]. www.hoovnews.hoovers.com/fp.asp?layout=displaynews&doc_id=idNR20010330290.2_85.

Catholic Health Initiatives. 2000. "2000 Annual Report." [Online retrieval 4/17/01]. www.catholichealthinit.org.

———. 2001a. "Who We Are." [Online retrieval 4/17/01]. http://www.catholichealth-init.org/body.cfm?ID=36917.

———. 2001b. "Catholic Health East and Catholic Health Initiatives Sign Letter of Intent for Transfer of Facilities." [Online article retrieval 4/17/01]. www.catholichealthinit.org/body.cfm?id=37543&action=detail&ref=16.

Connor, R. A., R. A. Feldman, B. E. Dowd, and T. A. Radcliff. 1997. "Which Types of Hospital Mergers Save Consumers Money?" *Health Affairs* 16(6): 62–74.

Elderweb. 2001. "Beverly Enterprises." [Online article retrieval 4/23/01]. www.elderweb.com/default.php3?PageID=852.

Hoovers Online. 2001a. "Aetna CFO Resigns; Stocks Fall Further." [Online article retrieval 4/16/01]. www.hoovershbn.hoovers.com/bin/story?StoryId+CoTPUqb9DtJe2nde2nJuX.

———. 2001b. "Bank of America Corporation." [Online article retrieval 3/12/01]. www.hoovers.com/co/capsule/4/0,2163,58444,00.html.

———. 2001c. "Catholic Health Initiatives." [Online article retrieval 3/13/01]. www.hoovers.com/co/capsule/3/0,2163,44843,00.html.

———. 2001d. "Beverly Enterprises, Inc." [Online article retrieval 3/13/01]. www.hoovers.com/co/capsule/1,0,2163,10211,00.html.

Infirmation Link Corporation. 2001. "BankAmerica Corporation Company Q&A." [Online article retrieval 4/17/01]. http://www.infirmation.com/shared/ company-qa/one.tcl?company_key=bankamerica&section=company.

Irving Levin Associates. 2001. "Hospital M&A Activity Slow in 2000 as Health Care Industry Begins to Stabilize." [Online article retrieval 4/18/01]. http:// levinassociates.com/pressroom/pressreleases/pr2001/pr103har7.htm.

Lutz, S. 1996. "Merger Would Form Utah Powerhouse." *Modern Healthcare* April 22: 14.

Lynk, W. J. 1995. "The Creation of Economic Efficiencies in Hospital Mergers." *Journal of Health Economics* 14 (5): 507–30.

Mercy Medical Center. 2001. "Mercy's Community Commitment Strengthened by National Ties." [Online article retrieval 3/13/01]. www.mercyrose.org/chi.html.

Reuters Company News. 2001. "Aetna's CFO Resigns in Midst of Company Woes." [Online article retrieval 4/16/01]. www.hoovershbn.hoovers.com/ bin/story?StoryId=CoTPUqb9DtJe2ndyZndK1.

Trespacz, K. 1999. "Bigger Is Not Always Better." *Managed Care Magazine.* [Online article retrieval 4/18/01]. http://managedcaremag.com/archives/9910/ 9910.consolidate.html.

Viscio, A. J., J. R. Harbison, A. Asin, and R. P. Vitaro. 1999. "Post-Merger Integration: What Makes Mergers Work?" [Online article retrieval 3/30/01]. http://www.strategy-business.com/bestpractices/9904/page1.html}.

Weil, T. P. 2000. "Horizontal Mergers in the United States Health Field: Some Practical Realities." *Health Services Management Research* 13 (3): 137–51.

Yafchak, R. 2000. "A Longitudinal Study of Economies of Scale in the Hospital Industry." *Journal of Health Care Finance* 27 (1): 67–89.

Yahoo! Finance Market Guide. 2001. "Profile—Beverly Enterprises." [Online article retrieval 4/23/01]. www.biz.yahoo.com/p/b/bev.html.

# CHAPTER 4

# Diversification

## INTRODUCTION

DIVERSIFICATION AS A competitive strategy has been applied under the rationale that it helps ensure the viability and sustainability of an organization's core business(es). In the healthcare industry, diversification began in earnest in the 1980s as organizations expanded into related businesses, most commonly profitable noncore business lines.

This chapter examines the effectiveness of diversification in nonhealthcare organizations and among healthcare providers. Literature reviews and case studies are included.

## DIVERSIFICATION DEFINED

Diversification can appear to be similar to vertical integration, but it is in fact quite different. Diversification is true to its name—the introduction of variety into the organization in the form of new services or entirely new businesses. Diversification by an organization might look similar to vertical integration, but as explained below, the intent of the expansion and methods to put it into operation are quite different. In healthcare, diversification has typically involved hospitals or systems expanding into related businesses, such as home care, nursing homes, retirement centers, etc. Diversification almost always results from acquisition of an existing entity but is occasionally accomplished by a new start-up venture.

The rationale for diversification is generally fivefold:

1. It fulfills the need to spread risk.
2. It presents an opportunity for higher profitability and return on investment.
3. It fulfills a desire for more rapid growth.
4. It creates greater market power.
5. It generates economies of scope.

## WHY DIVERSIFICATION?

Often at the heart of diversification is concern about the viability and sustainability of the company's core business. Even without this concern, however, in theory, the combination of a number of relatively independent business lines into one enterprise reduces the risk to the company from adverse conditions affecting any single business line. In healthcare, diversification has been most topical when margins are depressed in the core business and external pressures and change are great.

Especially in for-profit companies, but to some degree in not-for-profits as well, diversification is viewed as a way to increase overall company margins or profitability. Expansion into more profitable business lines (using the BCG type of analysis and others presented in chapter 1) in another industry should boost financial performance. In healthcare, diversification has occurred almost exclusively through investment in more profitable noncore business lines. Not-for-profits particularly and for-profits occasionally may use this increased profitability to subsidize the original or core business, sustaining more capacity or the business as a whole beyond the point at which a more prudent and objective investor might choose.

Connected to the drive for more profitability but with somewhat different intentions is the desire for more growth. Both motivations are characteristic of firms whose core business is growing slowly, stagnating, or declining. In addition to the direct financial benefits diversification may offer, growth provides opportunities for senior and other personnel within the company to enjoy increased responsibilities, job satisfaction, and, as is characteristic of larger companies, compensation levels. Growth may also be an aid in retaining or recruiting specialized personnel or acquiring specialized technology that the firm could not afford otherwise.

The market power rationale and benefits are least prevalent in healthcare and more characteristic of for-profit conglomerates. These very large diverse companies can gain advantage in three ways.

1. *Predatory pricing*—prices are lowered, often below cost, to gain market share and drive out competitors; American electronics firms accused Japanese firms of this strategy in the 1980s in the television market, and some small, local healthcare companies (in areas such as durable medical equipment) have accused large healthcare systems of such practices as recently as the late 1990s.
2. *Reciprocal buying*—according preference in purchasing to firms that are good customers for the megafirms' own products.
3. *Mutual forbearance*—large multiproduct companies encounter their competitors in a number of different product areas and may choose to avoid vigorous competition with each other and expend their competitive energies and resources in areas where they do not compete head to head; this strategy may also have the effect of stabilizing industries where conglomerates compete with one another.

Last, another potential benefit and competitive advantage from diversification are economies of scope in deployment of common resources. This benefit generally accrues from inputs to a production process that are used in two or more unrelated products and that allow the diversified firm to minimize production costs. Although economies of scope have some applicability in service companies, such as healthcare organizations, it is principally of benefit to manufacturers (Grant 1991).

## DIVERSIFICATION AS A COMPETITIVE ADVANTAGE

Diversification is an especially common competitive strategy outside of healthcare delivery and has also drawn considerable academic and public scrutiny over its effectiveness. Porter (1987 and 1998) presents research that demonstrates the lack of success of diversification, even by otherwise successful large companies. "[O]n average corporations divested more than half of their acquisitions in new industries and more than 60 percent of their acquisitions in entirely new fields . . . the track record in unrelated acquisitions is even worse—the average divestment rate is a startling 74 percent" (Porter 1987 and 1998). He adds:

> Competition occurs at the business unit level. Diversified companies do not compete, only their business units do. Unless a corporate strategy places primary attention on nurturing the success of each unit, the strategy will fail, no matter how elegantly constructed. Successful corporate strategy must grow out of and reinforce competitive strategy.

In a broad review of the literature on diversification, Grant (1991) agrees with and extends Porter's main points:

> Diversification is a corporate minefield. In no other area of corporate strategy have so many companies made such disastrous

investments. Ever since the 1960s, academics and business commentators have pointed to the dismal record of diversification by large companies; particularly those which have diversified by acquisition. Yet the diversification trend continues. . . Why does diversification seem to have such an irresistible attraction for companies, and what recommendations can be offered to improve the outcomes of diversification?

Grant (1991) suggests that the supposed competitive advantages of diversification need to be scrutinized more carefully in advance of proposed transactions. Can synergies such as the economies of scope described above and others actually be realized and will the "cost of managing the diversified corporation . . . not outweigh the benefits the diversification offers through the sharing of resources and skills"?

## DIVERSIFICATION CASE STUDIES

As noted above, diversification continues to be an active area in corporate America. The following examples help to illustrate some of the opportunities and pitfalls in diversification.

### Berkshire Hathaway Inc.

Berkshire Hathaway is the holding company for the diversified assets of billionaire Warren Buffett, one of the world's richest men. While the company serves primarily as a property and casualty insurance and reinsurance corporation, including National Indemnity, GEICO, and General Re, its other assets are far flung. Berkshire Hathaway owns stakes in Helzburg Diamonds, See's Candy, FlightSafety International, H.H. Brown and Dexter Shoe Companies, and an unusual array of other diversified businesses, mostly in the United States. In addition, Berkshire Hathaway has large stakes in American Express, Coca-Cola, Gillette, The Washington Post Company, Wells Fargo, and MidAmerican Energy (Hoovers 2001a).

## History

Buffett and his wife, Susan, own about 40 percent of Berkshire Hathaway, which is ranked number 40 on the *Fortune* 500 list of largest companies and number 14 on *Fortune*'s list of the most admired global companies (Hoovers 2001a). In the 36 years that Buffett has headed the company, its per-share book value has grown, on average, more than 23 percent per year. Notable company downturns have occurred, as in 1999, but the company rebounded in 2000, with net profits rising 113 percent to $3.3 billion (Chaffin 2001). In 32 of the 36 years, Berkshire Hathaway's per-share results have topped the total return of the S&P 500, sometimes substantially (Loomis 2001).

Buffett started the company with $500,000 in investments from family and friends in 1957. The partnership gained 251 percent in value in five years and 1,156 percent in ten years. When Buffett liquidated the partnership in 1969, Berkshire Hathaway Inc., originally a textile mill, became his investment vehicle (Jordon 2001). The firm has 112,000 employees and is headquartered in Omaha, Nebraska.

## Diversification Strategy

Berkshire Hathaway's acquisitions are undoubtedly diverse, leaving many in the business world puzzled by its success. According to Buffett, diversification is protection against ignorance, and in his usual wry commentary he notes that diversification may make little sense for those who know what they are doing. Berkshire Hathaway's typical strategy is to wait until a great company with predictable earnings growth is available at a discount price. The company also makes purchases without the use of derivatives, hostile takeovers, or leveraged buyouts, and it advocates investing in businesses that it will never want to sell. Most importantly, Berkshire Hathaway seeks out businesses in which it understands the product and the nature of the competition and then evaluates whether the earning power over the next 5 to 15 years is good and improving or poor and getting worse.

Other business strategies also are apparent in the company's acquisitions. For example, with the 1998 merger of Berkshire Hathaway and insurer General Re, four areas of synergy were cited as motivators for the merger: removal of constraints on earnings volatility, presentation of opportunities to develop the global reinsurance franchise, gains in tax flexibility, and offers of access to abundant capital (Berkshire Hathaway 1998).

Buffett's business acumen has been chronicled in 16 books, including 3 that have appeared in 2001. But he is quick to note his misjudgments. Berkshire Hathaway's annual report regularly lists his admitted errors, such as paying too much for Dexter Shoes in 1993 and then using Berkshire shares in the purchase. After Berkshire Hathaway's dismal performance in 1999, he stated that the company would have fared better if he had sneaked off to the movies while the stock market was open (Jordon 2001). Berkshire Hathaway has also sworn off investments in the airlines since its $358 million "mistake" in US Airways Group. Berkshire Hathaway acquired a stake in US Airways Group in 1989 and has since sold it, without saying whether it made money (Rothman 2001).

### Diversification May Bode Well for Stability

While many companies are bracing for an economic downturn, analysts believe that Berkshire Hathaway's diversified holdings will keep the firm stable. Specifically cited are the firm's insurance subsidiaries, which are demonstrating improved performance, and the potential array of acquisitions Berkshire Hathaway is considering to boost substantial growth (Pascavis 2001). In April 2001, Buffett told his shareholders that Berkshire Hathaway is "eager and ready" to make acquisitions of up to $20 billion (Cahill 2001).

Buffett's view of an ideal company is one that makes a steady profit, has excellent management, is available at a bargain price, and is protected against competition by an inherent advantage (Jordon 2001). Berkshire Hathaway also credits its sustainability to not investing in technology companies. Buffett has argued for several years that the Internet would create few new profits. He believes that one cannot predict how an individual company will perform in an emerging industry if there is no track record of consistent earnings or sense of long-term advantages (Jordon 2001). Instead, Berkshire Hathaway has set a course for the twenty-first century by investing in solid industries such as brick, carpet, insulation, and paint (Chaffin 2001).

The outlook is positive for Berkshire Hathaway, as demonstrated by Buffett's admirable track record of buying good companies at reasonable prices. In 2000, the firm doubled its normal rate of acquisitions (eight companies for $8 billion, paying cash for 97 percent of its purchases [Cahill 2001]), and in 2001, the pace was equally brisk. Berkshire Hathaway announced in April 2001 that it would purchase more than $10 billion in utility companies should some regulatory restrictions be removed that limit how much control holding companies can have in utilities. Partnering with Leucadia, Berkshire Hathaway has also purchased a $6 billion portion of insurer Finova Group (Pascavis 2001). Buffett has also set his sights on Europe, hoping to buy privately owned businesses. Buffett told his shareholders in early 2001: "We just haven't had any luck internationally and we hope that will change" (Larsen 2001).

Berkshire Hathaway, however, is hardly immune to economic calamities. Major losses among its insurers could damage short-term profitability, as in 1999. Berkshire's largest insurance subsidiary, General Re, experienced a massive operating loss in 2000 of $1.2 billion, but increases in premium rates should boost profitability. Cutbacks in an aggressive marketing campaign Berkshire launched for its auto insurer, GEICO, should increase profits for the firm. The advertising campaign failed to convert the level of inquiries into policies that had been anticipated (Pascavis 2001).

The firm's publicly traded securities, such as Coke and American Express, could also falter, but analysts continue to foresee positive outcomes for Berkshire stockholders (Pascavis 2001). For the quarter ending March 31, 2001, revenues rose 26 percent to $8.14 billion, setting the firm on a course for another successful year of profits from its array of investments.

## General Electric

General Electric has applied the concept of diversification and with it has proven it can succeed as the top or number two company in an eclectic mix of industries. A self-described diversified technology services and manufacturing company with annual revenues in 2000 of over $129 billion, General Electric operates in more than 100 countries with over 313,000 employees (General Electric 2001a). The company's origins lie with Thomas Edison who established Edison Electric Light Company in 1878. Edison's firm merged with Thomson-Houston Electric Company in 1892 to create General Electric Company, the only company listed on the Dow Jones Industrial index today that was also included in the original index in 1896.

The highly diverse company produces aircraft engines, locomotives and other transportation equipment, home appliances, lighting, generators and turbines, electric distribution and control equipment, medical imaging equipment, nuclear reactors, and plastics. It also has a financial division, GE Capital Services, which is one of the largest financial services divisions in the United States. General Electric also owns the National Broadcasting Company, Inc. (NBC), which serves 13 company-owned stations and more than

220 affiliates, operates cable channels CNBC and MSNBC, and holds partial ownership of a variety of other cable channels (Hoovers 2001b).

Major technological advances are the hallmark of General Electric. Recent breakthroughs include new imaging technology to assist with earlier diagnosis of cancer, the first noninvasive hemodynamic patient monitoring system, and a new "true light" light bulb. In fact, so vast is the General Electric empire, a press release is issued almost daily announcing a new technology or product release or major business transaction, including more than 100 acquisitions made in 2000 (General Electric 2001f).

General Electric's long, successful history has earned it many accolades. The most recent is being named "America's Most Admired Company" by *Fortune* magazine for the fourth consecutive year. *Fortune* cites General Electric's "Tireless innovation. Robust financials. The ability to lure and keep the smartest people" (General Electric 2001c).

The company is highly regarded for developing some of the best leaders in business, for committing about $500 million annually to training and education programs, and for developing the first major corporate business school for its leaders at a campus in the Hudson Valley of New York, which has been copied by other companies worldwide. Sometimes called the "Harvard" of corporate America, General Electric has pioneered business strategies such as MBO (management by objectives) and SWOT analysis (strengths, weaknesses, opportunities, and threats), which have been adopted extensively by businesses and governments worldwide.

### Strategies for Success

General Electric is probably most commonly respected for its ability to not stand still and be content with existing success, but to aggressively anticipate changes in market forces long before its competitors. One of General Electric's driving forces, which is included in its statement of values, is to "Act in a boundaryless fashion" (General Electric 2001e)—a tenet that encourages and receives participation from employees at all levels.

Several other key characteristics are often cited as major contributors to General Electric's success in diversified markets. Despite its massive size, the company strictly adheres to a few key issues: core values, financial targets, and a rigorous personnel review and promotion process. The company also launches major corporatewide initiatives such as globalization in the 1980s, a shift from products to products plus service in 1995, the Six Sigma quality program in 1996, and e-business in 1999, which company executives claim could save General Electric billions in just a few years.

General Electric has also been highly successful at taking its universal corporate culture, transplanting it overseas, and allowing local talent to grow the business to suit local conditions. The company has also excelled at buying companies and integrating them quickly into the General Electric culture. Their philosophy is that there are no mergers of equals, just acquisitions. In short, if you do not want to change, then do not be acquired (Rohwer and Windham 2000).

### Success Under a Proven Leader

Much of General Electric's success is credited to the guidance of Jack Welch, retired chief executive officer of the company. Although he gained the unflattering nickname Neutron Jack when he engineered the layoff of 100,000 employees from 1981 to 1985, he has undoubtedly moved General Electric from a staid institution to a dynamic and diverse powerhouse with his philosophy "If you're not number one or number two in your field, get out" (*Time* 2001). Under Welch's leadership, General Electric became highly productive by undergoing a complex reorganization that ultimately simplified the company into one with dominant positions in its carefully selected businesses.

Welch's guidance has allowed the company to be highly aggressive when opportunities have arisen. GE Capital packed its portfolio with real estate during the savings and loan crisis in the United States, was similarly relentless when the peso collapsed in Latin America, and has launched a formidable business expansion in Asia since the 1997 Asian financial crisis (Rohwer and Windham 2000).

Noteworthy scandals and setbacks also occurred during Welch's tenure, such as criminal indictments related to military contracts, criticism over General Electric's refusal to take action on PCB contamination in the Hudson River, and the 1994 bond trading scandal that led to huge losses (*Business Week* 2001).

Financially, General Electric is on track to deliver record performance in 2001. General Electric posted record earnings for the first quarter of 2001, achieving a 16 percent increase in earnings to $3.01 billion (General Electric 2001b).

According to new General Electric President and Chairman Jeffrey Immelt, "The strength of the GE model really shines during slower parts of the business cycle—our global diversity, service growth, quality efforts, and digitization efforts have reduced GE's sensitivity to business cycles" (General Electric 2001a). And General Electric appears poised to continue its successful run as a diversified yet united conglomerate in the twenty-first century.

## DIVERSIFICATION IN HEALTHCARE

Diversification among healthcare providers began in earnest in the mid-1980s. As a result of the prospective payment systems for inpatient care implemented by Medicare and increasing regulation, hospitals were concerned that operating margins in their core business would decline and many aggressively sought opportunities for profitability elsewhere, both within and outside of healthcare.

The search for new ventures was accompanied by restructuring among organizations to accommodate the new businesses at both the board and management levels. By the early 1990s, diversification was proclaimed a failure and most of the new ventures were divested or reduced in scope. Diversification as a central competitive thrust of healthcare organizations was replaced by horizontal and vertical integration and many of the related ventures that remained within healthcare organizations became candidates for integration, the newly emerging buzzword of the industry. As the trend toward integration began to wane in the late 1990s and operating margins began a precipitous decline, selective diversification once again became topical.

Duncan, Ginter, and Swayne (1995) identify and describe two types of diversification in healthcare (although these types do apply to other industries as well): related or concentric diversification and unrelated or conglomerate diversification. Related diversification, illustrated in Figure 4.1, often involves developing a group of related businesses around the hub or core business, thus in a concentric approach. Although related diversification assumes that some synergies are developed among the business entities, it is far different from vertical integration's basic rationale that is grounded in these synergies and attempts to tighten relationships among the entities. In contrast, unrelated diversification, also illustrated in Figure 4.1, involves developing a portfolio of separate products or services that, if operated in a relatively autonomous manner, would be similar to the conglomerates found in industry outside of healthcare.

Whereas diversification by for-profits is really an organizationwide or corporate strategy (and not directly relevant to individual business units), diversification by not-for-profits and by healthcare not-for-profits in particular is mainly a competitive strategy. The difference lies in the intent of the strategy, which among not-for-profits is largely to support the core business. In other words, diversification is used to buttress and strengthen core business lines in not-for-profits, especially in difficult times when competitive strategies carried out within the business units themselves might not be as successful.

**Figure 4.1: Related and Unrelated Diversification by a Primary Provider**

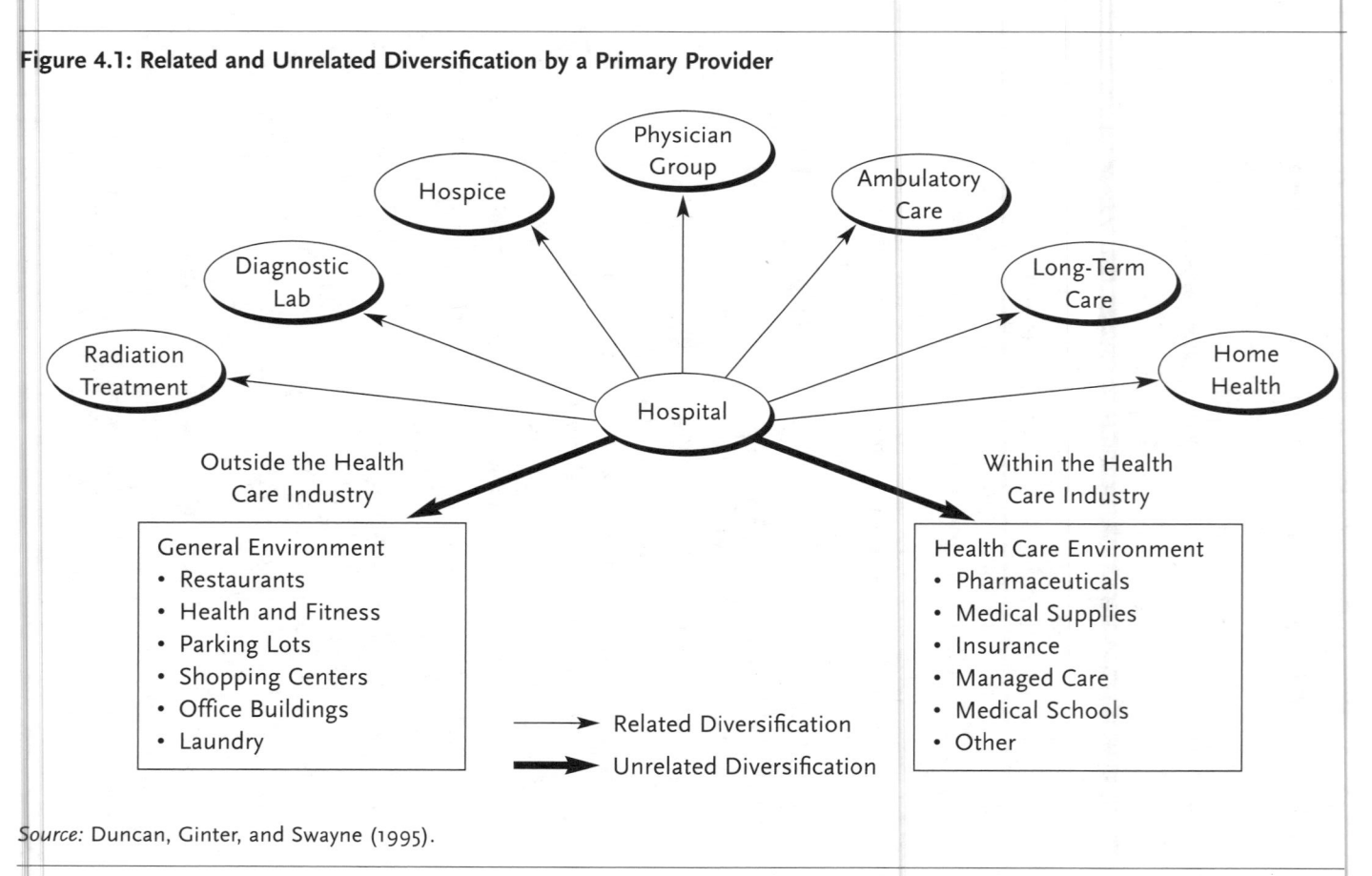

*Source:* Duncan, Ginter, and Swayne (1995).

The literature on the success of diversification in healthcare is only slightly more encouraging than the general business literature. Cleverley and Harvey (1992) studied the competitive strategies of 1,000 large U.S. urban hospitals and concluded that "[i]n general, greater diversification appears to be an effective strategy for improving financial performance," but "low market share hospitals should concentrate on their existing product lines before rushing into new product and market areas."

Subsequently, Eastaugh (1992) found that "excess diversification appears to exhibit the most rapid declines in profitability." Recently, Langabeer (1998) studied the competitive strategies of 100 major teaching hospitals in the United States and found that diversification had "virtually no recognizable influence on financial performance."

The findings of Shortell, Morrison, and Friedman (1990) on diversification may be the most telling for healthcare organizations:

> In general, we found that the more related the diversification activity, the more likely it was to be profitable . . . we also found, however, that partially related diversification efforts, such as home healthcare, long-term care, and ambulatory care centers, were successful if (1) the different technical, managerial, and cultural requirements of the services were recognized, (2) resources and attention were concentrated in a few well-selected areas, and (3) market-entry strategies were appropriately matched to the specific activity.

In contrast to the experience outside of healthcare where acquisition and development internally are almost the exclusive methods that companies use to diversify, Shortell and colleagues suggest:

> [i]n partially related diversification, where one does not possess all the resources to develop this service, a joint venture or network relationship with others has advantages: the opportunity to share costs and risks and the opportunity to learn from each other.

"Intermediate entry strategies, halfway between doing it oneself and entering into a joint venture with an outside party" could also have applicability to healthcare diversifiers (Shortell, Morrison, and Friedman 1990).

Finally, Clement (1988) reviews the diversification experience of companies outside of healthcare and suggests five lessons for healthcare managers to increase the likelihood of financially successful diversification:

1. Diversification does not guarantee higher profitability.
2. Diversification does not reduce total risk.
3. Related diversification seems to result in better financial performance than unrelated.
4. Financial benefits from diversification may take time to be realized.
5. Market conditions affect success—especially high market growth, high market share, and low competition are associated with higher profitability.

The following case studies illustrate healthcare organizations that have experienced varying degrees of success in diversification and illustrate how this strategy is applied and the nature of its competitive benefits.

## UniHealth America

UniHealth America was one of the first integrated healthcare delivery systems in the United States and was at one time considered a premier model of integration. Although referred to in its own publications as a vertically integrated healthcare delivery system, the media often referred to UniHealth as a diversified healthcare system. In retrospect, UniHealth strived for but never achieved true integration and its diversity was ultimately its undoing.

UniHealth America, headquartered in Burbank, California, was originally formed through hospital mergers in the Los Angeles area. Early initiatives illustrate its commitment to both diversification and vertical integration. UniHealth played a key role in forming PacifiCare Health Systems in the mid-1970s, which emerged at one point as the nation's largest Medicare risk plan. UniHealth also formed the Care America HMO and was one of the first systems to acquire medical group practices and develop tax-exempt medical foundations (Robinson 1996).

A 1992 speech by Paul Teslow, UniHealth's president and chief executive officer, noted that UniHealth had four goals: to regionally integrate, to be quality and value driven, to merge care and financing, and to create continuums of care. He noted that UniHealth had achieved these goals, in part, through strategic alliances among physicians, payers, hospitals, providers of specialized services and products, suppliers, and employers (Teslow 1992).

### Vertical Integration and Diversification Strategies Fail

The expected synergies and efficiencies of a vertically integrated system proved elusive for UniHealth. UniHealth hospitals never served as the principal inpatient providers for PacifiCare or CareAmerica, leaving the system with the appearance of a corporate holding company rather than a cohesive provider of health-care and insurance services (Robinson 1996).

UniHealth tried to gain focus in the early 1990s, retaining only a minority share in PacifiCare and pursuing diversification, primarily through multispecialty medical groups and independent practice associations (IPAs). Rather than expanding its hospital holdings, UniHealth sold them when possible in favor of expanding the geographic reach of its capitated physician groups. These groups were not acquired with the goal of generating inpatient admissions for UniHealth hospitals, and, in fact, many of the medical groups and IPAS were located in markets where UniHealth did not have inpatient facilities (Robinson 1996). Instead, the practices were viewed as the "crown jewels" of the organization's shift to a physician-based network management company.

UniHealth's diversification strategy backfired, ultimately leading to financial losses from which UniHealth could not recover. Despite its control of large blocs of physicians, industry watchers noted that UniHealth, as a not-for-profit organization, lacked the capital to compete with the well-heeled physician practice management firms (Shinkman 1997) and was hampered by the lack of profitability in its hospitals, resulting in a massive financial debt of more than $330 million by 1998 (Shinkman 1998). Many also questioned UniHealth's ability to effectively manage the physician groups. In 1997, the Personal Choice Medical Group in San Jose, California, filed a lawsuit against UniHealth, claiming that its affiliation was causing the group to lose money (Delevett 1998).

### Disintegrating the System

In late 1998, after nearly a year of negotiations, the hospital division of UniHealth, consisting of eight hospitals in the Los Angeles area, merged with Catholic Healthcare West (CHW) to give CHW a total of 48 hospitals across California. The sale of the hospitals along with the November 1997 sale of the CareAmerica HMO to Blue Shield of California for $165 million (Rauber 1999), signaled the beginning of UniHealth's strategy of complete divestment of the $1.5 billion organization, which at one point operated 11 hospitals, managed a panel of 7,100 physicians, owned an HMO and was a majority stockholder of an insurance carrier, and had operations in home health, dialysis, and hospice care (Rauber 1997). The proceeds from the sales were used to create a large charitable foundation, now known as the UniHealth Foundation (Rauber 1999).

Despite its demise, there were sparks of innovation in the UniHealth system. In 1992, the organization initiated a process for continuously reviewing and monitoring the value of its hospitals, medical groups, health plans, and other lines of business. While asset evaluation processes are common among American corporations and some investor-owned hospitals, it was a new concept for most not-for-profit healthcare providers. UniHealth developed its own process for determining the baseline value of its subsidiaries and establishing goals for increasing the value of each asset. The system also devised a process for monitoring events called "trigger points," which could affect the value of the asset, and an options analysis, which would present alternatives to pursue if a trigger point occurred (Pallarito 1995).

Following the April 1992 Los Angeles riots, the UniHealth America Foundation launched Heal L.A., a program that raised more than $150,000 to help riot victims. The program was the most comprehensive person-to-person intervention program following the riots and received more than a dozen regional and national awards.

But a few innovative strategies and goodwill gestures could not save one of the fastest growing health systems in California. And as with other pioneers in the new world of integrated healthcare delivery, its missteps at vertical integration and diversification were costly and ultimately fatal.

## Joslin Diabetes Center, Inc.

Joslin Diabetes Center, Inc., is world renowned as the leader in diabetes research, patient care, and training. During its 101-year history, the organization has grown to be the world's largest institution dedicated to diabetes and has established a strong reputation for excellence in patient care and research (Guidestar 2001). Among its most notable recent achievements have been laser treatment for diabetic eye disease, reduced complications for pregnant women with diabetes, and discovery of methods for detecting diabetes before it develops.

*Organizational Structure*

The organization is divided into three divisions. The Joslin Clinic is a multispecialty group practice that handles all aspects of diabetes care including genetic counseling, eye care, nephrology, podiatry, nutrition, and exercise. The second division is the Elliott P. Joslin Research Laboratory. With 12 lab sections and a $25 million annual budget, it is dedicated to researching diabetes causes and complications (Guidestar 2001). A third division focuses on Joslin's national and international activities, including the Joslin diabetes franchises across the country (Joslin Diabetes Center 1998).

The nonprofit organization, with an annual budget of $63 million, employs more than 500 staff members, including internationally recognized scientists. Joslin is a member of the Harvard Medical School teaching network and has trained more than 900 diabetologists who now practice in 40 countries (Guidestar 2001).

At the organization's original location in Boston and at its Massachusetts satellites, 75,000 patients are seen each year. Joslin has diversified beyond its home base and currently operates at 24 affiliate centers nationwide (including a joint venture with the Boston area CareGroup system of hospitals and other providers) that see an additional 90,000 patients annually (Guidestar 2001). Joslin's comprehensive disease management model is credited with keeping yearly costs for diabetes patients 50 percent lower than the national average, even though Joslin's patient mix includes many insulin-using patients and patients with preexisting complications (Joslin Diabetes Center 1998).

In 1998, with the founding of the organization's national and international division, Alan M. Jacobson, M.D., became Joslin's first senior vice president for strategic business initiatives, signaling the organization's intent to focus on the diabetes care franchises, continuing medical education programs for physicians (currently reaching more than 30,000 medical personnel annually), federal initiatives to develop diabetes care programs for the U.S. Department of Defense and the Veterans Administration, and a telemedicine initiative. These programs are aimed toward further developing Joslin's national and international system of diabetes services and generating significant new income to support the organization's research and patient care activities (Joslin Diabetes Center 1998).

These initiatives follow a period of rapid growth for the organization. Joslin's annual budget rose from $17.2 million in 1987 to $63 million in 2000, and its endowment has grown to $45 million (Joslin Diabetes Center 2000).

## Initiatives for Growth

Joslin aims for sensible growth. In 2000, the organization had one of its most successful years, posting a 15 percent increase in its budget (Joslin Diabetes Center 2001b). Initiatives in 2001 include becoming an educational partner with Diabetes Direct, a home delivery service for diabetes testing supplies, medications, products, and support services. Joslin will provide news and educational information on diabetes care for Diabetes Direct's catalogues, newsletters, and web site. (Yahoo!Finance 2001). Other objectives for 2001 include further fostering collaboration and synergy among the multidisciplinary scientists who are employed by Joslin or work in a collaborative capacity with the organization.

With 16 million Americans currently diagnosed with diabetes and marked increases in the prevalence of diabetes occurring worldwide,

Joslin's diversified base of diabetes programs and services is poised to continue a steady pattern of growth and sustain widespread reimbursement cutbacks currently occurring and on the horizon.

## CONCLUSION

Diversification has achieved modest success outside of the healthcare industry and limited success among healthcare providers. As a result of the disastrous experiences with diversification in healthcare delivery in the late 1980s and early 1990s, few instances exist in healthcare today where diversification is being followed as a principal strategy.

The experience of UniHealth is typical of healthcare diversifiers that migrate into far-flung ventures that accelerate the erosion of their core businesses rather than support it. The case of Joslin, in contrast, indicates that related diversification can be successful.

Like vertical integration, diversification is a high-risk, high-reward strategy. As such, it probably is one that is inappropriate for nearly all healthcare organizations.

## REFERENCES

Berkshire Hathaway. 1998. "Berkshire Hathaway Inc. and General Re Corporation to Merge." [Online article retrieval 5/14/2001]. http://www.berkshirehathaway.com/news/jun1998.html.

*Business Week.* 2001. "Jack: The Welch Era at General Electric." [Online article retrieval 6/18/01]. http://www.businessweek.com:/2000/00_50/b3711013.htm?script.

Cahill, T. 2001. "Buffett on Quest for the Perfect Takeover." *Bloomberg News,* April 30. [Online article retrieval 6/16/01]. http://seattletimes.nwsource.com/cgi_bin/texis.cgi/web/vortex/display?slug=berkshirecash30&date=20010430&query=warren+buffett.

Chaffin, J. 2001. "Buffett Chides Tech Investors." *Financial Times,* March 11. [Online article retrieval 6/12/01]. www.ft.com.

Clement, J. B. 1988. "Corporate Diversification: Expectations and Outcomes." *Health Care Management Review* 13 (2): 7–13.

Cleverley, W. O., and R. K. Harvey. 1992. "Competitive Strategy for Successful Hospital Management," *Hospital and Health Services Administration* 37 (1): 53–69.

Delevett, P. 1998. "San Jose Medical to Break Ties with UniMed, UniHealth." *San Jose Business Journal,* September 11, 1998. [Online article retrieval 8/20/01]. http://sanjose.bcentral.com/sanjose/stories/1998/09/14/story7.html.

Duncan, W. J. , P. M. Ginter, and L. E. Swayne. 1995. *Strategic Management of Health Care Organizations,* 2nd edition. Boston: Blackwell Business.

Eastaugh. S. R. 1992. "Hospital Strategy and Financial Performance." *Health Care Management Review* 17 (3): 19–31.

General Electric. 2001a. "GE Board Authorizes Regular Dividend." [Online retrieval 6/20/01]. http://ge.com/news.

———. 2001b. "GE Reports First-Quarter 2001 Results—Ongoing Earnings Up 16 Percent to $3.017 Billion—Industrial Earnings Up 11%. [Online retrieval 6/20/01]. http://ge.com/news.

———. 2001c. "GE Named America's Most Admired Company by *Fortune* Magazine." [Online retrieval 6/20/01]. http://ge.com/news.

———. 2001d. "GE Leadership & Training." [Online retrieval 6/20/01]. http://www.ge.com/news.

———. 2001e. "Mission." [Online retrieval 6/20/01]. http://www.ge.com/new/podium_papers/mission.htm.

———. 2001f. "Letter to Share Owners." GE 2000 Annual Report. [Online retrieval 6/19/01]. http://www.ge.com/annualoo/letter/index.html.

Grant, R. M. 1991. *Contemporary Strategy Analysis.* Cambridge, MA: Basil Blackwell, Inc.

Guidestar. 2001. "Joslin Diabetes Center, Inc." [Online article retrieval 4/26/2001]. www.guidestar.com.

Hoovers. 2001a. Berkshire Hathaway Inc. [Online article retrieval 5/14/01]. http://hoovers.com/co/capsule/6/0,2163,10206,00.html.

———. 2001b. General Electric Company. [Online article retrieval 5/16/01]. http://www.hoovers.com/co/capsule/4/0,2163,10624,00.html.

Jordon, S. 2001. "Short Course on Warren Buffett." *Omaha World-Herald,* April 27. [Online article retrieval 6/16/01]. http://new.Omaha.com/index/php?u_div= 3&u_hdg=2&u_sid=93885.

Joslin Diabetes Center. 1998. "Joslin Names New Senior Vice President." [Online article retrieval 5/16/2001]. http;//www.joslin.org/news/jacobpr.html.

————. 2000. "C. Ronald Kahn, M. D., Named Sixth President of Joslin Diabetes Center." [Online article retrieval 5/16/2001]. http://www.joslin.org/ news/new_president.html.

————. 2001a. "Joslin Affiliation Opportunities." [Online article retrieval 5/16/2001]. http://www.joslin.org/jnationwide/developing/brochure_section1. html.

————. 2001b. 2000 Annual Report. [Online retrieval 5/16/01]. http://www. joslin.org/annual_report/index.html.

Langabeer, J. 1998. "Competitive Strategy in Turbulent Healthcare Markets: An Analysis of Financially Effective Teaching Hospitals." *Journal of Healthcare Management* 43 (6): 512–25.

Larsen, P. T. 2001. "Buffett Looks to Europe for Expansion: World's Wealthiest Investor Hopes to End His Run of International Bad Luck." *Financial Times,* April 20. [Online article retrieval 6/16/01]. www.ft.com.

Loomis, C. J. 2001. "The Value Machine." *Fortune,* February 19. [Online article retrieval 6/12/01]. www.fortune.com.

Pallarito, K. 1995. "California Not-for-Profit Maximizes Its Assets." *Modern Healthcare,* August 19. [Online article retrieval 8/20/01]. www.modernhealth-care.com/archive/members/articles/1995/06/19_7616.php.

Pascavis, T. 2001. "Berkshire Hathaway Should Fare Well in Downturn." [Online article retrieval 6/12/01]. http://news.morningstar.com/news/Wire/0,1230,5220,00. html.

Porter, M. E. 1987 and 1998. "From Competitive Advantage to Corporate Strategy." *Harvard Business Review,* May/June 1987, in Michael E. Porter. 1998. *On Competition.* Boston: Harvard Business School Publishing.

Rauber, C. 1997. "Hospital Giant CHW in Talks with UniHealth." *San Francisco Business Times,* December 22, 1997. [Online article retrieval 8/20/01]. http://sanfrancisco.bcentral.com/sanfrancisco/stories/1997/12/22/story3.html.

————. 1999. "UniHealth Working to Reinvent Itself." *Modern Healthcare,* May 10. [Online article retrieval 8/20/01]. www.Modernhealthcare.com/archive/ members/articles/1999/05/10_3655.php.

Robinson, J. C. 1996. "The Dynamics and Limits of Corporate Growth in Health Care." *Health Affairs* 15 (2): 155–69.

Rohwer, J., and L. Windham. 2000. "GE Digs into Asia." *Fortune,* October 2. [Online retrieval 6/20/01]. http://www.fortune.com/indexw.jhtml?channel= artcol.jhtml&doc_id=00000570.

Rothman, A. 2001. "Buffett Says He Has Sworn Off Airline Stocks." *Bloomberg News,* March 29. [Online article retrieval 6/16/01]. http://archives.seattletimes. nwsource.com/cgi-bin/texis.web/vortex/browse?month=03&day= 29&year2001.

Shinkman, R. 1997. "Reversal of Fortune: RFP Signals Big Changes Are Ahead for UniHealth." *Modern Healthcare,* November 3. [Online retrieval 8/21/01]. www.modernhealthcare.com/archive/members/articles/1997/11/03_13245.php.

————. 1998. "UniHealth Hospitals to Merge with CHW." *Modern Healthcare,* October 19. [Online retrieval 8/20/01]. www.modernhealthcare.com/archive/ members/articles/1998/10/19_15615.php.

Shortell, S. M., E. M. Morrison, and B. Friedman. 1990. *Strategic Choices for America's Hospitals: Managing Change in Turbulent Times.* San Francisco: Jossey-Bass.

Smilgis, M. 2001. "Warren Buffett at Age 71: A High-Tech Kinda Guy?" *San Francisco Examiner.* [Online article retrieval 6/16/01]. http://www.examiner. com/business/default.jsp?story=b.investor.0412w.

Teslow, P. 1992. "Healthcare Providers' Success May Depend on Collaboration." Speech at the 77th Annual Catholic Health Association Assembly. [Online retrieval 8/21/01]. http://www.chausa.org/PUBS/PUBSART. ASP?ISSUE=HP9207&ARTICLE=AG.

*Time.* 2001. "People of the Year 2000." [Online article retrieval 6/22/01]. http:// www.time.com/time/poy2000/pwm/welch.html.

Yahoo!Finance. 2001. "Joslin Diabetes Center Partners with Diabetes Direct." [Online article retrieval 5/16/01]. http://biz.yahoo.com/bw/010417/2556.html.

# CHAPTER 5

# Niching

## INTRODUCTION

PURSUIT OF NICHE markets, referred to in this book as *niching,* is a competitive strategy that has achieved great success outside of the healthcare industry. Niching is now making inroads as a successful strategy for healthcare providers as well, particularly among for-profit companies that are exploiting opportunities in targeted market segments that hospitals and systems have overlooked or have deemed too small to pursue.

This chapter examines the competitive advantages and disadvantages of this strategy and provides guidance on how to identify niches and realize their potential benefits. Case studies of organizations outside the healthcare field and within the healthcare industry illustrate the potential benefits and pitfalls of this strategy.

## NICHING DEFINED

A niche or focus strategy identifies a narrow segment of the market and develops the firm's products or services and marketing and sales activities to meet the needs of this segment. In so doing, the firm may (East Carolina University School of Business 2000):

- "Choose a market niche where buyers have distinctive preferences, special requirements or unique needs" or
- "Develop a unique ability to serve needs of target buyer segments."

An example from Michael Porter's writings (1996) further illustrates the niching concept:

> A focused competitor, such as Ikea [the Sweden-based global furniture company that targets young furniture buyers who want style at low cost], targets the special needs of a subset of customers and designs its activities accordingly. Focused competitors thrive on groups of customers who are overserved (and hence overpriced) by more broadly targeted competitors, or underserved (and hence underpriced). A broadly targeted competitor —for example, Vanguard [the mutual funds company] or Delta Air Lines—serves a wide array of customers, performing a set of activities designed to meet their common needs. It ignores or meets only partially the more idiosyncratic needs of particular customer groups.

## NICHING IN HEALTHCARE

Niching has a long history in healthcare. The movement from the general practice of medicine to specialization and, more recently, subspecialization is probably the best example of how this strategy has been deployed in healthcare. Hospitals, nursing homes, home care agencies, and other healthcare organizations also have all employed niche strategies to varying degrees. Most recently, niching has been employed by for-profit companies in healthcare to exploit opportunities in very targeted market segments.

Niche strategies are often used by new firms trying to break in to what appears to be an overcrowded and overserved market. The new firm identifies a segment that may have been overlooked or underdeveloped and focuses its attention, energies, and products or services on this segment. Niching is also commonly used by existing organizations that try to capitalize on untapped markets; however, unless the existing company truly develops and operates a separate business unit dedicated to the niche identified, successful execution of the niche strategy is likely to be incomplete at best. In most instances, in fact, a niching strategy never really materializes and may be subsumed within the broader strategic orientation of the larger organization.

## NICHING STRATEGY IN ACTION

Niche strategies are based on the premise that a customer group with like needs exists in the market, that this group is large enough to support a focused business, and that the group has some common needs that have not been well served by existing firms in that market (see Figure 5.1). Competitive advantage occurs when a product or service responds effectively to identified needs in a way that is not readily replicable by other firms or is focused on such a small segment that it does not attract the attention and competitive responses of the larger firms in that industry (see Figure 5.2).

Many niche firms start out by attempting to serve such small segments that the large firms in that industry are not concerned about the new start-up. If the niche firm is successful, it may broaden its product offerings somewhat or its geographic reach. At this point, many niche firms begin to be noticed by competitors. Competitor responses and the effectiveness of those responses vary and some firms survive, while others do not. Many niche firms, at this stage, are acquired by competitors, which often signals the end of their ability to function effectively as a niche business.

### Figure 5.1: What Makes a Segment Attractive for Focusing?

- The segment is big enough to be profitable but small enough to be of secondary interest to large rivals.
- There is good growth potential in the industry with many fast-growing segments.
- The segment is not crucial to the success of major competitors, and preferably, no other rivals concentrate on this segment.
- Niching firm has resources to effectively serve the segment.
- Niching firm can defend itself against challengers via customer goodwill and its superior ability to serve buyers in the segment.

*Source:* Reprinted, with permission, from "Strategy and Competitive Advantage," East Carolina University School of Business course material. Copyright © 2000.

## Benefits

Although not the intent of most niche businesses at the outset, it is often possible to grow these businesses horizontally to the point where they develop economies of scale and, occasionally, some market power. Niche businesses that start out by serving a limited geographic market may gain economies if they can significantly expand the geography served. Sometimes this expansion is accomplished by acquisition of like entities operating in other geographic markets, whereas in other instances it is accomplished by internal expansion. If the niche business can achieve a dominant position in the segment in which it is operating, real market power and revenue advantages can also result.

## Disadvantages

The main disadvantages of the niche strategy are that the market may be too small to support a viable business, the opportunity to develop a truly differentiated product or service may not prove to

**Figure 5.2: When Does a Focus Strategy Work Best?**

- It is costly or difficult for multisegment rivals to serve specialized needs of target niche.
- No other rivals are concentrating on same segment.
- Firm's resources do not permit it to go after a wider portion of market.
- Industry has many different segments, creating more focusing opportunities.

*Source:* Reprinted, with permission, from "Strategy and Competitive Advantage," East Carolina University School of Business course material. Copyright 2000.

---

be available, and large competitors may respond effectively and use their size to crush the upstart. In certain cases, the emergence of the niche firm attracts a number of like new firms and the market may not be large enough to support some or all of the niche competitors. Finally, some niche firms flounder when they mature, either because they lose their focus as they attempt to expand or stagnate after successfully penetrating the niche to some degree.

## Niching in High-Growth and High-Technology Industries

Niche strategies have been especially prevalent in the past decade in new and high-growth industries and especially high-technology industries. A recent study of 166 entrepreneurial, technology-based firms sponsored by the Research Institute for Small and Emerging Business (1997) found that:

> firms that choose to reduce the complexity of their technology-based industries by becoming highly focused on a narrow niche, and which pursue a complementary focused planning process, create a synergy between strategy and strategy planning

that facilitates performance. Apparently, focused planning supports the high degree of strategic focus implied by the niche strategy, leading to an efficient use of resources and rapid decision making.

Further, the study "emphasizes that, to be successful, cutting-edge firms must find a strategy appropriate to the industry and resources of the firms—never losing sight of their target niche. Conversely, firms lacking a clear pattern of niche strategy and planning focus are more likely to perform poorly" (Research Institute for Small and Emerging Business 1997).

### Niching in Mature and Declining Industries

Niche strategies are also fairly common in mature and declining industries. Porter suggests that there are four basic strategies for firms in declining industries—leadership, niche, harvest, or divest quickly (see Figure 5.3)—all of which need to be viewed in the context of the firm's strategic need to remain in the business (Porter 1987 and 1998).

> When, because of low uncertainty, low exit barriers, and so forth, the industry structure is likely to go through an orderly decline phase, strong companies can either seek leadership or defend a niche, depending on the value to them of remaining market segments. . . When high uncertainty, high exit barriers, or conditions leading to volatile end-game rivalry make the industry environment hostile, investing to achieve leadership is not likely to yield rewards. If the company has strengths in the market segments that will persist, it can try either shrinking into a protected niche, or harvesting, or both.

With these perspectives as background, the following case studies illustrate the power of the niching strategy.

**Figure 5.3: Competitive Strategies for Declining Businesses**

| | Has competitive strengths for remaining demand pockets | Lacks competitive strengths for remaining demand pockets |
|---|---|---|
| Favorable industry structure for decline | Leadership or niche | Harvest or divest quickly |
| Unfavorable industry structure for decline | Niche or harvest | Divest quickly |

*Source:* Reprinted by permission of *Harvard Business Review*. From "From Competitive Strategy to Corporate Strategy" by M. E. Porter, May/June 1987, in Michael E. Porter, *On Competition*. Copyright © 1998 by the Harvard Business School Publishing Corporation; all rights reserved.

## Nokia

Nokia is considered one of the world leaders in mobile communications, in part by making the Internet mobile for individuals and corporations. The company has grown from a fledgling venture in the heretofore undeveloped business of mobile communications (i.e., a new niche) in the 1980s into a large, far-flung enterprise. With net sales of $27 billion in 2000, over 60,000 employees, listings on six major exchanges, production locations in 10 countries, research and development underway in 15 countries, and active sales in over 130 countries (Nokia 2001), there is little doubt that Nokia has set its sights on dominating the mobile communications industry and outmaneuvering established competitors, including AT&T, GTE, and Motorola. The firm was recently ranked number eight in *Fortune* magazine's most admired global companies (Hoovers 2001a.)

Nokia's watchwords are innovation and design, experience, user-friendliness, reliable solutions, and customer satisfaction. Despite its size, the organization has a flat, nonhierarchical operational structure that Nokia believes stimulates entrepreneurism and risk taking.

## Structure

The firm is segmented into four units. Nokia Networks is a supplier of video and voice networks and related services and is considered a leader in developing mobile Internet applications. Nokia Networks is the leading supplier of GSM systems, which are the global systems for mobile communications. Nokia provides GSM technology to 102 operators in 46 countries. Nokia Mobile Phones is the world's largest mobile phone manufacturer. Nokia Ventures Organization, with $650 million under management, invests in wireless technology start-ups and develops new entrepreneurial ventures that may fall outside of Nokia's usual business offerings but help the firm stay in touch with early developments in the Internet economy and any signs of a weakening marketplace. Last, the Nokia Research Center focuses on creating new technologies that combine Internet and mobile communications (Nokia 2001).

These business segments enhance Nokia's reputation as a complete supplier. Nokia Mobile Phones, accounting for 72 percent of Nokia sales (Hoovers 2001a), has built a solid reputation as a supplier of user-friendly, high-quality phones, while Nokia Network provides the systems and infrastructure for the analog and digital networks that are the platforms for mobile phone use.

The ventures organization and research center are designed to ensure that the firm has a balanced portfolio of new and sustainable businesses to support future growth.

## A History at the Cutting Edge Leads to the Digital Telecommunications Niche

Nokia has been at the forefront of using leading-edge technologies since its inception in 1865. Starting out as a Finnish manufacturer of the first communications medium—paper—the company then moved into rubber and associated chemicals (Finnish Rubber Works). In 1912, Finnish Cable Works was formed to capitalize on the movement of electricity into homes and factories and then the manufacturing of cables for the telegraph industry and eventually the telephone. In 1960, an electronics department was set up at the Cable Works, paving the way for formation of Nokia Corporation in 1967—a merger of Nokia Company (the original paper-making company) and Finnish Rubberworks and Finnish Cable Works (Nokia 2001).

Nokia has prided itself on its ability to set trends, particularly in the area of product design. In the 1960s, when all rubber boots were black, the rubber division started making boots in bright colors. More importantly in the 1960s, Nokia entered the telecommunications market, developing a radio telephone and data modems long before the general public dreamed of such items. In the 1980s, Nokia was a major producer of computers, monitors, and televisions, but developments were underway that would change the company's direction. In 1981, the world's first international cellular mobile telephone network was launched in Scandinavia and Nokia made the first car phone for the new network (Nokia 2001).

Nokia went on to develop the original handheld portable phone in 1987. With the widespread deregulation that stimulated competition and increased consumer expectations, Nokia was adept at adapting, quickly focusing the company's entire operations on the niche of digital telecommunications. With the advent of digital technology, data messages far exceed voice communications by volume, and Nokia has set the standard for enabling consumers to read e-mails and transfer files by connecting mobile phones to computers (Nokia 2001).

Nokia Senior Vice President Kari Ahola stated that Nokia's major transformations were possible because of the company's "sense of agility and daring in restructuring itself at the right time to take advantage of opportunities as they come" (Asia Intelligence Wire 2001).

Nokia will need to continue with its forward-thinking strategies as a new market opens up with the arrival of the third-generation (3G) mobile radio, which will be capable of carrying voice, data, text, and graphics in real time or as stored information. According to Nokia Vice President Christian Kurten, the highly competitive 3G market ". . . will be a battle, right from day one." Nokia is hoping that the more than 100 operator customers that use its second generation (2G) network equipment and will have to adapt to the 3G technology will give Nokia an edge as the competition heats up (Nokia 2001).

Despite its successful operations and stellar reputation, there have been notable flaws in Nokia's products. Rumors in April 2001 indicated that Nokia might need to launch a massive recall of mobile phones. About 25 percent of its mobile phones have a software glitch that prevents them from connecting to 3G wireless networks, although Nokia claims it can fix the glitch without a recall (Batista 2001).

*Customer Loyalty Key to Securing Nokia's Niche*

Nokia is counting on its loyal customer base to secure its future success. Customer loyalty is sought by programs such as Club

Nokia, designed to keep customers informed of new developments in games, music, and imaging that are available to mobile phone users. The club, with several million members, features a web site to support customer interaction and includes call center support and service backup. The goal of Club Nokia, according to Markus Nilsson, senior manager of Club Nokia, is to "create customer loyalty by establishing an emotional bond through continuous dialogue" (Nokia 2001).

With projections that over one billion people will use mobile phones by 2002, customer loyalty will be key and competition will be relentless. And market growth is slowing as more people acquire phones, although growth levels are still attractive. In addition, the product life cycle for a mobile phone is around two years, meaning the replacement market holds great potential. Specifically, Nokia envisions more market segmentation, with handsets and services tailored to meet individual needs. Nokia likens the market to buying a car. With a first car purchase, the consumer may elect for a basic model. As the consumer becomes more knowledgeable of brands and features, they are likely to become loyal to a brand (Nokia 2001). In terms of Nokia's product offerings, this philosophy translates into manufacturing phones that surf the Internet and can be used to purchase stock offerings to selling brightly colored mobile phones with game functions for the youth market.

Financially, Nokia is demonstrating strong financial performance in a highly competitive market. Operating profits increased by 48 percent in 2000 to EUR 5.8 billion (Nokia 2001). In 2000, net sales were up 54 percent and earnings per share rose 50 percent. In comparison, Nokia's chief rivals, Motorola and Ericcson, have failed to turn profits on their phones (Reuters 2001). Ericcson experienced a 52 percent drop in sales from April 2000 to April 2001, which translated into a loss of $560 million (Stanton 2001).

Nokia was able to improve internal productivity in 2000, increasing its workforce by only 9 percent despite a 54 percent increase in revenues. With Nokia's phenomenal revenue growth in 2000, the firm increased its investments in research and development by 47 percent, with nearly one-third of Nokia staff working in research and development. The competitive nature of mobile technology and an increase in economic uncertainty will undoubtedly influence Nokia's future prospects. An estimated 40 multinational companies now have the capability to make mobile phones (Morais 2001).

In June 2000, Nokia's stock was at $62.50, making it Europe's most valuable company. As of March 2001, Nokia's stock had dropped to $21, cutting $190 billion from its valuation (Morais 2001). A recent report by investment bank Nomura questions whether Nokia is capable of making the transition to wireless data and postulates that Nokia may be another IBM. "For all of IBM's excellence, it failed to successfully migrate into the new world. Now the mobile phone industry, both its operators and equipment makers, faces challenges every bit as momentous" (Morais 2001). Yet Nokia believes that its basic ideology of strategically focusing on the niche of digital telecommunications will lead to successful rollout of new products and services, supported by the firm's longstanding reputation for reinventing itself to fit the market.

### Gannett Company, Inc.

Gannett Company, Inc., is a multibillion-dollar international news and information company that publishes newspapers and operates broadcasting stations. Headquartered in Arlington, Virginia, and employing 53,400 people, Gannett is the nation's largest newspaper group in terms of circulation in the United States. Its 99 daily newspapers have a combined daily paid circulation of 7.8 million.

But it is the media powerhouse, USA *Today,* the country's first national, general interest daily newspaper, that has put Gannett on the map. Started in 1982, USA *Today* has filled a largely untapped niche and now has a circulation of about 2.3 million in 60 countries worldwide (Gannett 2000). USA *Today* competes with the *Wall*

*Street Journal* for the number one national daily ranking by circulation (Hoovers 2001b), but the focus and tone of the papers are quite different. USA *Today* and its spinoff, USA *Weekend,* which is carried in 555 newspapers, have pursued a much more contemporary approach to news and information with a substantial focus on entertainment and lifestyle issues. The *Wall Street Journal* maintains its longstanding position as a more traditional paper with longer, more serious business-related and investigative articles.

## A Long History of Innovation

Gannett's origins date back to 1906 when Frank E. Gannett and associates bought a half interest in the *Elmira Gazette* in Elmira, New York. Other newspapers were added through the years. In 1923, when the holdings included six newspapers in upstate New York, Frank Gannett bought out his partners and formed the Gannett Company, Inc. During the next 25 years, 15 more newspapers and 7 radio stations were added to the company. The use of innovative technology in the company was evident from early on. In 1929, Frank Gannett invested in the development of a teletypesetter. Gannett newsrooms were equipped with shortwave radio sets to speed up reporting, and printing presses were adapted for color as early as 1938 (Gannett 2001).

With the death of Frank Gannett in 1957, Paul Miller was elected president and chief executive officer. Miller is credited with moving Gannett from a regional newspaper group to a more national focus. The company went public in 1967. Since the 1970s, Gannett has pursued steady growth and diversification through mergers (Gannett 2000). Its signature publication, USA *Today,* was launched at a time when skeptics were vocal about the demise of daily newspapers (Gannett 2001).

Gannett is exhibiting strong financial performance, posting its ninth consecutive year of record revenue in 2000 and its thirty-first year of record profits since the company went public in 1967. Revenues in 2000 were $6.2 billion, a 22 percent increase over 1999. Gannett credits its strong financial performance to solid advertising demand, the Olympics, election-related ad spending, and a variety of strategic acquisitions (Gannett 2000).

*Leveraging the National News Niche with the Internet*

Gannett's underlying strategy demonstrates that newspapers are valuable and trusted sources of news and information whose credibility will be enhanced by the Internet. The USA *Today* web site is ranked the number one newspaper site on the Internet, with 2.4 billion pages viewed in 2000, which is a 50 percent increase over total traffic in 1999. Advertising and other revenue from Internet activities totaled approximately $62 million in 2000, up from $39 million in 1999 (Gannett 2000).

Initiatives are underway to attract and keep readers—the constant challenge of the print medium—through better content and new products. Gannett News Service launched "e" in 2000, which is a weekly guide to personal technology, aimed at helping people use technology to make their lives better and more entertaining. A Generation X task force of Gannett employees was formed to find new ways to attract and retain readers ages 25 to 34 (Gannett 2000).

Technology is changing time-honored newspaper printing methods. USA *Today* recently eliminated the use of film at all of its production sites, giving newsrooms later deadlines and facilitating delivery of newspapers to circulation departments earlier (Gannett 2000).

Technology is also spurring the development of joint projects among Gannett's divisions. In June 2000 at the national political conventions, USA TODAY LIVE was launched as a multimedia venture that produces the content of USA *Today* in electronic format and distributes it to the Gannett television stations for exclusive segments in news reports and to USATODAY.com, which streamed audio and video to Internet users worldwide. Gannett intends to leverage these capabilities fully by convincing news sources that stories will appear in the largest newspaper, on one of the largest web sites, and on the largest local affiliate television station group (Gannett 2000).

With a solid year of financial performance in 2000, Gannett plans in 2001 to "aggressively go after revenues through better products and smart deals. And we'll use our financial discipline to deliver a solid performance." This challenge will be formidable as the slowing economy and higher newsprint expenses are on the horizon. First quarter 2001 advertising revenues for *USA Today* declined 20 percent from the previous year (Gannett 2001) leading to about 100 layoffs since January 2001 and the first newsroom layoffs since the paper's founding (*Financial Post* 2001).

However, Gannett was the only large, publicly traded newspaper published not to issue a profit warning for the first quarter of 2001, although Gannett Chairman and Chief Executive Officer Douglas McCorkindale cautions that Gannett is operating as if it were in or about to enter a recession (Dow Jones Newswires 2001).

And what seems to be Gannett's magic touch at turning a profit is not always well received by employees and readers who say journalistic quality and integrity are harmed by Gannett's demands for higher earnings. Readers and writers complain of poor news judgment, ignored national and world affairs, and shorter stories to make room for graphic elements. Still others claim that Gannett has proven that a high-quality national newspaper can be produced that also makes money. And Gannett claims that its proven strategies show that it is listening to readers and controlling costs to help the company flourish (Gissler 1997).

With predictions that the print medium would die a slow death with the advent of the Internet now proven false, Gannett, despite its detractors, appears poised to be a key player in the national news and information industry with its shrewd business acumen and ability to meet the new demands of a national readership.

Despite its long history of successful application in healthcare delivery, niching has been somewhat out of vogue until very recently. The integrated delivery system movement and many of the previous unsatisfactory experiences in diversification relegated niching to a minor role in not-for-profit healthcare. And yet, in many ways the rise of big healthcare delivery organizations is exactly what provided the impetus for the return of niching as an important and successful strategy for healthcare providers.

Coincident with these developments was the emergence of the venture capital funds, the economic boom in America, and the increased availability of relatively "easy money" looking for places to earn good returns. Healthcare has proven to be one of these places where significant investments were made from 1995 to 2000, leading to the development of many for-profit niche providers.

### Niche Players

Probably the most notable, but not successful, group of new niche players in healthcare delivery has been the physician practice management firms. The physician practice management sector was created in the early and mid-1990s to consolidate the fragmented physician practice field and exploit opportunities for economies and market power by bringing together groups of physicians under one corporate umbrella. In addition, practices owned by the physician practice management companies had purported advantages of access to capital, development of important information technology, and other less significant, but nonetheless highly touted competitive advantages over the remaining physicians in practice. Few of these benefits ever materialized and many of the physician practice management companies failed, while those that remain in business have had to restructure and reorganize to remain viable.

A second group of new niche players arose in ambulatory care. These firms have been developed largely to exploit small and growing segments of ambulatory care delivery that have been previously undeveloped. Examples of new niche players in these areas are:

- AmSurg Corporation: a firm dedicated to developing and operating practice-based ambulatory surgery centers with physician groups
- American WholeHealth, Inc.: a company that develops alternative/complementary care centers
- Gerimed: a company that develops outpatient senior care centers

Nationally, many local and regional ophthalmologic practices have stepped forward to take advantage of the opportunities in vision correction, using lasers and new procedures made possible by technological advancements. Most metropolitan areas now have surgical centers specializing in vision correction; as recently as 1995, few of these centers existed nationally.

According to a report in *Hospitals and Health Networks* (Greene 1997),

[t]oday's risk capital increasingly flows to companies that manage care. . . In the past 10 years or so, venture capital was focused on developing HMOs, outpatient surgery, rural hospitals, and major consolidation of existing business. . . But now that we're approaching the next millennium, it's focused much more on actual medical management.

## NICHING CASE STUDIES

Many niche firms in healthcare delivery today effectively illustrate how this concept is being applied in the field. The following case studies profile two niche firms, one not-for-profit that redefined its role in a declining segment of the market to be a more focused niche operation, and a for-profit in a traditional healthcare service area.

## Wills Eye Hospital

Wills Eye Hospital in Philadelphia, Pennsylvania, has evolved into one of the world's leading providers of ophthalmology services. The organization's clinical departments serve more patients and perform more surgical procedures in the hospital and in its network of surgery centers than any other eye care provider in the country. The independent, not-for-profit institution draws its vast base of patients from worldwide referrals that enable Wills to gather significant clinical data and participate in numerous research projects (Wills 2001).

Wills Eye Hospital was established in 1832 as the first eye hospital in the Western Hemisphere and thus played a key role in establishing ophthalmology as a separate branch of medicine. Founded through a bequest of James Wills, a Quaker merchant, the nonprofit specialty institution has established a reputation for world-renowned clinical expertise and diagnostic and treatment procedures. Wills has been ranked for nine consecutive years as one of the nation's best hospitals by the *U.S. News & World Report*. The hospital currently has 500 physicians on its medical staff and 660 employees (Wills 2001).

Wills' physicians have pioneered the development of many special techniques and instruments that are now commonplace in the practice of ophthalmology. The first implantation of an artificial intraocular lens to replace lenses affected by cataracts and development of a vitrectomy machine now used for microsurgery are among the landmark developments. Research at Wills is carried out in the laboratories of the hospital's research department, established in 1952, and in cooperation with a number of national organizations and government agencies (Wills 2001). Wills is also home to the

Philadephia area's only Gamma knife and has one of only two specially designed machines dedicated to head surgery (Hollreiser 1997).

Originally established with 70 beds, the hospital moved to new quarters in 1932 to expand its inpatient bed capacity to 120 and add space for outpatient services and conference and teaching facilities. Subspecialty services were added starting in the 1960s. In 1980 the hospital moved to a new facility that is twice the size of its former quarters (Wills 2001). In 1999, in response to the rapidly shrinking inpatient market, Wills announced plans to sell its hospital facility and build a smaller, $40 million facility across the street to house what will still be called a hospital, but will in essence be a large surgical center with physician offices, emergency care, ancillary services, and educational training space. Some rooms for short-stay patients will also be included (George 1999). In the ten-year period from 1985 to 1995, ophthalmology admissions decreased by almost 50 percent at Wills. And from 1995 to 1997, they fell an additional 26 percent. The new facility is expected to better position Wills for this restructured market.

The full range of eye problems are treated at Wills—from common problems to rare sight-threatening diseases. In addition to general eye care, Wills offers nine subspecialty areas that include such services as cataract and primary eye care, contact lens service, cornea service, glaucoma service, neuro-ophthalmology services, oculoplastic care, ocular oncology service (one of the largest in the world), pathology, pediatric ophthalmology, and a retina service. The hospital also provides refractive surgery, a center for the study of eye movement in children, a sports vision center, a low vision center, and a 24-hour emergency department (Wills 2001).

### Securing the Outpatient Specialty Surgery Niche

In 1995, Wills established a surgical network to provide convenient and low-cost ambulatory surgery centers throughout a three-state area. These nine community-based, same-day surgery centers perform almost every type of outpatient eye surgery, including laser vision correction surgery. This outpatient surgery network is emerging as a key niche market as Wills is largely redefining itself as an outpatient specialty surgery provider, rather than an inpatient hospital.

Wills' network of ambulatory surgery centers position the organization as a niche leader in the outpatient market, which may eventually account for 95 percent of all ophthalmology procedures. In addition, physician ownership is being planned at each of the ambulatory surgery centers. The centers' financial impact was immediate. With the first centers opening in 1995, they contributed 4,000 of the 14,000 total surgeries performed by Wills in the fiscal year ending June 1996. Wills hopes to eventually reach between 25,000 and 30,000 surgeries per year. The outpatient centers are also serving as feeders to the hospital, with each outpatient resulting in two to three referrals of patients that normally would not have used Wills' specialized services (Hollreiser 1997). Ambulatory surgery volume is unlikely, though, to generate a substantial number of inpatient cases, and Wills is setting its sights almost exclusively on the growing outpatient market.

### AmSurg Corporation

AmSurg Corporation is a successful acquirer, developer, and operator of practice-based ambulatory surgery centers created in partnership with physician groups in the United States. As of March 2001, the corporation owned a majority interest in 87 surgery centers concentrated heavily in California, Florida, Ohio, and Tennessee. Most centers specialize in surgeries that are generally high volume and low risk: 54 perform gastrointestinal endoscopy procedures, 28 perform ophthalmology surgery procedures, one center performs orthopedic procedures, one center performs otolaryngology procedures, and three centers perform surgeries in more than one specialty (biz.yahoo.com 2001a).

Headquartered in Nashville, Tennessee, the corporation was founded in 1992 to develop, acquire, and manage single-specialty ambulatory surgery centers and specialty physician networks in partnership with physicians. In 1997, American Healthcorp spun off AmSurg as a public company. Today AmSurg is the only publicly traded pure-play surgery center company and its success has been remarkable. Revenues for 2000 increased 41 percent compared to 1999, with earnings up 29 percent (AmSurg 2001).

In October 2000, AmSurg was ranked 139 on the *Forbes* listing of the "200 Best Small Companies" (AmSurg 2001). The corporation credits its success to focusing on the delivery of low-cost, high-quality surgery services that create value for the patient, physician, and payer. Patient satisfaction surveys show an astounding 99.7 percent overall satisfaction rate with AmSurg (AmSurg 2001).

### Single-Specialty Centers and Their Benefits to Physicians

AmSurg's partners are generally entities owned by physicians who perform procedures at the center. Through strategic planning sessions with its physician partners, AmSurg focuses on achieving market dominance and operating excellence at the local level. From AmSurg's perspective, single-specialty ambulatory surgery centers can provide physicians with new sources of revenue for cases they are already performing, and because a single-specialty center has fewer owners than a multispecialty center, income derived per physician-owner from a single-specialty center is greater. Single-specialty centers also claim to enhance physician productivity and lower costs through dedicated surgical teams, better scheduling, and quick room turnaround time (AmSurg 2001).

AmSurg publicizes an attractive list of benefits for its physician partners: national presence, aligned financial incentives, proven track record of reducing overhead, aggressive marketing plans, and equal representation in governance. In addition, AmSurg assumes responsibility for construction, state licensing,

Medicare certification, third-party payer negotiations, and many other management responsibilities that often plague practicing physicians (AmSurg 2001).

## Plans for Future Niche Growth

The corporation's plans for future expansion are to continue developing and acquiring additional practice-based ambulatory surgery centers in targeted specialties. Recent acquisitions include the purchase of a portion of Physicians Resource Group's ownership interest in outpatient ophthalmology surgery centers for $40 million. In another business deal with Physicians Resource Group in March 2001, AmSurg purchased eight surgery centers for approximately $37.5 million, with the possibility that several additional centers may be purchased in the future (biz.yahoo.com 2001a).

AmSurg's revenue is derived from the facility fees charged for surgical procedures. Fees vary depending on the procedure but usually include charges for operating room usage, special equipment, supplies, recovery room usage, nursing staff, and medications. Approximately 39 percent of AmSurg's net revenues come from governmental healthcare programs, mostly Medicare (biz.yahoo.com 2001a). Physicians keep 100 percent of the professional fees associated with the procedure and a portion of the facility fee (Guzman 2000).

Recent financial reports show strong performance for AmSurg. Revenue for the first three months of 2001 was $45.1 million, a 43 percent increase over the same period in 2000. This marks the 13th consecutive quarter of record revenues and record earnings since the company went public. Increases are credited to the new centers AmSurg added in 2001 and 12 percent revenue growth from existing centers, primarily derived from increases in procedure volumes. These increases follow three consecutive years of double-digit percentage increases in the corporation's existing centers. These strong early results for 2001 have led the firm to predict 22 to 25 percent growth in diluted earnings per share in 2001 (biz. yahoo.com 2001b).

New payment rates for outpatient surgery set by the Department of Health and Human Services may be phased in starting in January 2002. AmSurg predicts that these new rates would cut their annual revenues by 4 percent, but the corporation hopes to offset these potential losses with cost efficiencies at the center and corporate level (biz.yahoo.com 2001a). The corporation also cites projections that over the next five years, 90 percent of all elective surgeries will be performed on an outpatient basis (Guzman 2000). With 12 centers in development and a potential target of 1,200 practices where three or more doctors without a surgery center practice in specialties targeted by AmSurg, the corporation sees huge growth potential on the horizon (Wall Street Transcript 2001).

## CONCLUSION

Niching has demonstrated success both in the healthcare industry and in other business endeavors. It is being exploited quite successfully by for-profit enterprises in healthcare delivery but is still in its early phases of deployment by not-for-profit organizations in selected product or market segments. Niching's use and applicability are likely to grow, especially as large healthcare organizations shift from a corporate integrated delivery mentality to a more focused, customer-oriented product line mind-set.

## REFERENCES

AmSurg. 2001. "About AmSurg." [Online article retrieval 6/4/01]. http://www.amsurg.com.

Asia Intelligence Wire. 2001. "Weekender: RP Should be Quick to Raise Competitiveness, or Else. . ." [Online article retrieval 5/29/01]. http://www.nokia.com.

Batista, E. 2001. "Nokia Scrambles to Fix Glitch." [Online article retrieval 5/29/01]. http://www.wired.com/news/wireless/0,1382,42960,00.html.

biz.yahoo.com. 2001a. "AmSurg Corp Quarterly Report (SEC form 10Q). [Online retrieval 6/4/01]. http://biz.yahoo.com/e/010515/amsgb.html.

————. 2001b. "AmSurg Corp. First-Quarter Revenues Increase 43 Percent, on 12 Percent Growth in Same-Center Revenues." [Online article retrieval 6/4/01]. http://biz.yahoo.com/bw/010418/2522.html.

Dow Jones Newswires. 2001. "*USA Today* Confirms 5% Staff Cut Since the Start of the Year." [Online article retrieval 5/30/01]. http://business.com.

East Carolina University School of Business. 2000. Course materials: "Strategy and Competitive Advantage." [Online retrieval 1/7/2000]. www.business.ecu.edu/users/simerlyr/PPT2862.htm.

*Financial Post.* 2001. "Newsprint Costs Blamed for Staff Cuts at San Jose. *USA Today.*" [Online article retrieval 5/30/01]. http://www.hoovers.com.

Gannett. 2000. *2000 Annual Report.* [Online retrieval 5/15/01]. http://www.gannett.com.

————. 2001. "Company History." [Online article retrieval 5/30/01]. http://www.gannett.com/map/history.htm.

George, J. 1999. "Wills Eye to Sell Hospital, Build Another." *Philadelphia Business Journal,* November 11. [Online article retrieval 6/4/01]. http://philadelphia.bcentral.com/philadelphia/stories/1999/11/29/story4.html.

Gissler, S. 1997. "What Happens When Gannett Takes Over." *Columbia Journalism Review,* November/December. [Online article retrieval 5/30/01]. http://www.cjr.org/year/97/6/gannett.asp.

Greene, J. 1997 "Starting Up the Upstarts." *Hospitals and Health Networks.* December 20, 1997.

Guzman, S. 2000. "Do One Thing, Do It Well." [Online article retrieval 6/4/01]. http://www.surgerybiz.com/0300surg/storysurg0300.cfm.

Hollreiser, E. 1997. "Wills Eye Hospital at Turning Point as Industry Landscape Changes." *Philadelphia Business Journal.* [Online article retrieval 6/4/01]. http://philadelphia.bcentral.com/philadelphia/stories/1997/01/20/story2.html.

Hoovers. 2001a. "Nokia Corporation," [Online article retrieval 5/29/01]. http://www.hoovers.com/co/capsule/0/0,2163,41820,00.html.

————. 2001b. "Gannett Co., Inc." [Online article retrieval 5/30/01]. http://hoovers.com/co/capsule/3/0,2163,10623,00.html.

Morais, R. C. 2001. "Damn the Torpedoes." *Forbes,* May 14. [Online article retrieval 5/29/01]. http://www.forbes.com/forbes/2001/0514/100.html.

Nokia. 2001. "Who We Are." [Online article retrieval 5/29/01]. http://www.nokia.com/insight/who_we_are/index.html.

Porter, M. E. 1987 and 1998. "From Competitive Advantage to Corporate Strategy." *Harvard Business Review,* May/June 1987, in Michael E. Porter. 1998. *On Competition.* Boston: Harvard Business School Publishing.

———. 1996. "What is Strategy?" *Harvard Business Review* November/December: 67–68.

Research Institute for Small and Emerging Business. 1997. "Niche Strategy and Planning Focus—A Recipe for Success." [Online article retrieval 1/7/00]. www.riseb.org.

Reuters. 2001. "Nokia Looks to Asia, Youth to Retain Lead." [Online article retrieval 5/29/01]. http://news.cnet.com/news/0-1004-200-5822440-2.html?tag=1h.

Stanton, F. W. 2001. "Stocks on the Move: Nokia Trumps Ericsson Again." [Online article retrieval 5/29/01]. http://news.morningstar.com/news/Wire/0,1230,5156,00.html.

Wall Street Transcript. 2001. "CEO Speaks About the Size of the Market for AmSurg." [Online article retrieval 6/4/01]. http://www.twst.com/notes/articles/lar249.html.

Wills. 2001. Wills Eye Hospital web site. [Online retrieval 6/4/01]. http://www.willseye.org.

CHAPTER 6

# Cost Leadership

## INTRODUCTION

ACHIEVING COMPETITIVE ADVANTAGE through lower costs
is one of three generally recognized ways for a firm to compete
successfully over the long run (Porter 1980). Along with differentiation, the subject of the next chapter, and niching, the subject
of the preceding chapter, cost leadership also is regarded as an
excellent approach for creating competitive advantage. Through
a literature review and case studies, this chapter presents the benefits and drawbacks of implementing a cost leadership strategy.

## COST LEADERSHIP DEFINED

Low costs alone can provide some strategic advantage, but only
cost leadership—that is continuously producing products or services at a lower cost than competitors—can offer the potential for
a sustainable competitive advantage. In healthcare, the value of
cost leadership has been a hotly debated subject, as the discussion
of the healthcare literature that follows shortly will demonstrate.

Historically, low costs have been viewed as leading to low quality, and virtually no demand exists for low-quality healthcare. Also, healthcare reimbursement methodologies have provided little, if any, incentive for low costs until fairly recently. Nonetheless, the recent more difficult economic environment in healthcare seems to have sparked renewed interest in the value of a low-cost strategy.

Robert Grant (1991) provides an historical perspective of the role of cost in the arsenal of competitive strategies used by American businesses in the late twentieth century:

> Historically, business strategy analysis has emphasized cost advantage as the primary basis for competitive advantage in an industry. This focus on cost advantage reflects the traditional emphasis on price as the principal medium of competition among firms—competing on price depends ultimately on cost efficiency. It also reflects some of the principal strategic preoccupations of large industrial corporations. For much of the twentieth century, the strategies of large corporations have been driven by the quest for economies of scale and scope through investment in mass production and mass distribution. Since the mid-1980s, cost efficiency has remained a priority, but the focus has shifted toward cost cutting through restructuring, downsizing, outsourcing, "lean production," and the quest for dynamic rather than static sources of cost efficiency.
>
> For some industries, cost advantage is the predominant basis for competitive advantage: for commodity goods and services there are few opportunities for competing on dimensions other than cost. But even where competition focuses on product differentiation, intensifying competition has resulted in cost efficiency becoming a prerequisite for profitability. Some of the most dramatic examples of companies and industries being transformed through the pursuit of cost efficiency are in sectors where competition has increased sharply due to deregulation, such as airlines, telecommunications, banking, and electrical power generation.

# BENEFITS OF COST LEADERSHIP

To begin this review of the benefits of a low-cost competitive strategy, it is helpful to return to the work of Michael Porter (1985) and his initial framework of the three generic competitive strategies:

> Cost leadership is perhaps the clearest of the three generic strategies. In it, a firm sets out to become *the* low-cost producer in its industry. The firm has a broad scope and serves many industry segments, and may even operate in related industries—the firm's breadth is often important to its cost advantage. The sources of cost advantage are varied and depend on the structure of the industry. They may include the pursuit of economies of scale, proprietary technology, preferential access to raw materials, and other factors. . . .

Grant (1991) emphasizes the importance of understanding and influencing the underlying cost drivers that determine a firm's unit costs (see also Figure 6.1):

- *Economies of scale*—Increases in the amount of inputs yield a more than proportionate increase in total output. Scale economies, while usually associated with manufacturing operations, are also important in purchasing, research and development, distribution, and advertising.
- *Economies of learning*—Experience gained in particular jobs reduces the time, waste, and defects in completing the job. The more complex a process or product, the greater the potential for learning. Learning occurs both for the individual through improvements in dexterity and problem solving and at the group level through the development and refinement of organizational routines.
- *Process technology*—Generally a variety of ways may be used to produce a good or service. The method that results in production at significantly lower unit costs, either by using fewer inputs or a more cost-effective combination of inputs,

**Figure 6.1: The Drivers of Cost Advantage**

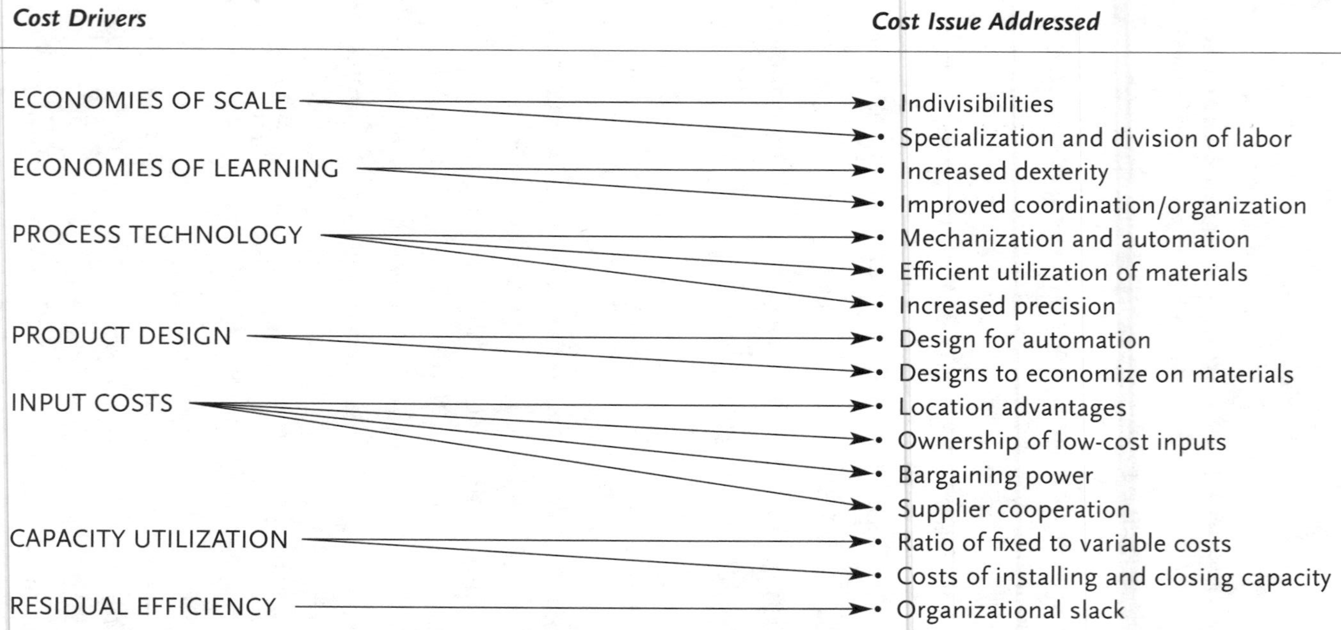

| Cost Drivers | Cost Issue Addressed |
|---|---|
| ECONOMIES OF SCALE | Indivisibilities |
| | Specialization and division of labor |
| | Increased dexterity |
| | Improved coordination/organization |
| ECONOMIES OF LEARNING | Mechanization and automation |
| | Efficient utilization of materials |
| | Increased precision |
| PROCESS TECHNOLOGY | Design for automation |
| | Designs to economize on materials |
| PRODUCT DESIGN | Location advantages |
| | Ownership of low-cost inputs |
| INPUT COSTS | Bargaining power |
| | Supplier cooperation |
| CAPACITY UTILIZATION | Ratio of fixed to variable costs |
| | Costs of installing and closing capacity |
| RESIDUAL EFFICIENCY | Organizational slack |

*Source:* Grant (1991).

has superior process technology. This advantage is often derived from new and improved capital equipment or substantial changes in organization and management.

- *Product design*—Designing products for ease of production can offer substantial cost savings, especially when linked to the introduction of new process technology.
- *Process design*—Reorganizing production processes even without new investment in capital or process innovation can result in substantial efficiency gains. Business process reengineering, the commonly used name for this concept, is based on the belief that most production and administrative processes are very complex and have evolved over time with little conscious or consistent direction. Redesigning such processes can achieve major gains in efficiency, quality, and speed.
- *Capacity utilization*—In businesses with large amounts of fixed assets (e.g., production plants, hospitals), the ability to use the assets to their capacity can significantly reduce unit costs. While consistent underuse of capacity raises unit costs, consistent overuse of capacity also may have a negative impact on unit costs through premium and overtime pay, increases in defects and errors, and higher maintenance costs.
- *Input costs*—Differences in the costs incurred by different firms for similar inputs can be a critical source of overall cost advantage. Differences may be attributable to geographic variation in input prices, ownership of low-cost suppliers, relationships with suppliers, nonunion labor, and bargaining power.
- *Residual efficiency*—Even after all of the major cost drivers are taken into account, unexplained differences in unit costs among competitors may remain. Residual efficiencies refer to the ability of the company to eliminate those costs (often characterized as "organizational slack") that allow the firm to approach its optimal operation. Firms faced with bankruptcy or those with highly motivated employees are those that may tap into this advantage.

Cost drivers determine the firm's cost position relative to its competitors. Both the effect of the individual cost drivers on a given product line or business unit and the interaction across business units or product lines affect the firm's cost position. According to Porter (1985), "[a] firm has a cost advantage if its cumulative cost of performing all value activities is lower than competitors' costs. The strategic value of cost advantage hinges on its sustainability. Sustainability will be present if the sources of a firm's cost advantage are difficult for competitors to replicate or imitate."

Sustainability is dependent on a number of factors. Entry or mobility barriers that constrain competitors from imitating the firm's behavior are one important source. The number of cost advantages has a major impact on sustainability. Certainly, advantages derived from some drivers, such as scale and proprietary product or process technology, are more important than others. And finally, the interaction among and synergies derived from the cost drivers can significantly increase the likelihood of sustainability. Porter (1996) suggests that "the whole matters more than any individual part. Competitive advantage grows out of the *entire system* of activities. The fit among activities substantially reduces cost or increases differentiation." (This concept then applies both to this chapter on cost leadership and to the next chapter on various aspects of differentiation.) Figure 6.2 summarizes the advantages and disadvantages of a cost leadership strategy.

So far, this chapter has been silent on the subject of pricing. Pricing, though obviously important to the firm's success, is tactical rather than strategic. Pricing does not offer the potential for sustainable advantage, is easily imitated (and often is), and does not address any of the fundamental aspects of the firm's operations on which to gain sustainable advantage. Therefore, while pricing is important and can assist in maximizing short-term profitability, it will not be addressed extensively in this chapter.

**Figure 6.2: Advantages and Disadvantages of a Cost Leadership Strategy**

**When a Low-Cost Provider Strategy Works Best**

- Price competition among rivals is dominant competitive force
- Industry's product is a commodity-type item readily available
- Few ways to achieve product differentiation that has value to buyers
- Most buyers have similar needs/requirements
- Buyers incur low switching costs changing sellers
- Buyers are large and have significant bargaining power

**Drawbacks to a Low-Cost Provider Strategy**

- Technical breakthroughs open up cost reductions for rivals, negating a low-cost provider's efficiency advantages
- Rivals find it comparatively easy or inexpensive to imitate leader's low-cost methods
- Low-cost provider becomes so fixated on cost reduction it fails to respond to
    - Increased buyer desires for added quality or service features
    - New developments in related products
    - Declining buyer sensitivity to price

*Source:* Reprinted, with permission, from "Strategy and Competitive Advantage," East Carolina University School of Business course material. Copyright © 2000.

## COST LEADERSHIP CASE STUDIES

The following case studies illustrate the ways in which a low-cost strategy can be pursued and the advantages and disadvantages it offers.

### Vanguard Group

In the highly competitive world of investment management firms, the Vanguard Group has staked its claim as the only company owned by its shareholders. With Vanguard's funds structured as independent investment companies that are owned by the share-holders, all management, administrative, and marketing services for the funds are provided on an at-cost basis (Careerbuilder Network 2001).

The funds of a typical mutual fund firm are usually controlled by an external management company that is owned by an individual, partnership, or investors who purchase the firm's publicly traded stock. The management company then charges fees, sometimes substantial ones, for management, administration, and marketing from which the company derives profits for its owners (Vanguard 2001a).

Vanguard's unique organizational structure gives it the industry's lowest cost-to-manage ratio and ensures that all profits are returned to its shareholders (Careerbuilder Network 2001). According to Lipper Inc., in 1999 Vanguard's funds cost on average 0.27 percent of assets, which is less than one-fourth of the mutual fund industry average of 1.31 percent. From Vanguard's perspective, these figures represent the strategic advantages of providing large cost savings and aligning their funds' operations with shareholder interests (Vanguard Group 2001a).

Vanguard also outsources management to other companies to reduce costs on its actively managed funds (Hoovers 2001a). According to John Brennan, chairman and chief executive officer, "It's rare to find a company that offers both the highest service quality and lowest fees, but we're able to do that because we have a unique corporate structure. We are a *mutual* mutual fund company, existing only to serve our mutual fund shareholders, and that translates into 'Unmatchable Value for Investors'" (Vanguard Group 2001b).

### A History of Steady Growth as a Cost Leader

Founded in 1975 and headquartered in Valley Forge, Pennsylvania, the company manages more than 100 different investment portfolios with over $550 billion in assets for 14 million clients. Vanguard also offers a variety of other services, including brokerage services, financial planning, and individual and employer retirement plans.

Vanguard's objective from the firm's inception has been to "provide top-performing, high-quality investment products and services at the lowest reasonable cost," according to Brennan. In addition to being a leader in low-cost investing, Vanguard was also the first company to offer a variety of tax-managed funds, offer index stock and bond mutual funds, and give investors a choice of low-cost bond funds with specific maturity ranges (Vanguard Group 2001c).

Its status as the leading low-cost investment firm has translated into superior financial performance. Net assets for Vanguard have risen from $1.8 billion in 1975 to more than $550 billion in 2000. But as the nation's second largest mutual fund firm, Vanguard claims its goal is to get better not bigger through expanded offerings and more sophisticated technology and managerial systems (Vanguard Group 2001c).

Vanguard's outstanding performance has merited it numerous accolades, including high honors from *Forbes, Fortune, Money,* and *Worth*. Vanguard dominated *Forbes'* 2000 "Best Buy" rankings, with 28 out of 66 funds in the listing managed by Vanguard. In 2001, the company was ranked sixth on *Computerworld's* "100 Best Places to Work" and was named to *Fortune's* "100 Best Companies to Work For."

Given Vanguard's extraordinary success with its low-cost reputation in an industry known for excessive fees, Vanguard appears well-positioned to continue on its path of maintaining the highest levels of quality and customer service at the lowest cost.

## Southwest Airlines

In another industry known for high costs, Dallas, Texas–based Southwest Airlines has established itself as the premier low-cost, no frills airline in the United States. And its profitable track record over 28 consecutive years demonstrates that its positioning is attracting a loyal following. Serving 58 airports in 29 states and operating more than 2,750 flights each day, the company has several key strategies for keeping costs down. To control maintenance and training costs, the airline only uses Boeing 737s. Southwest also operates its own reservation system and offers ticketless travel to help control back-office costs (Hoovers 2001b). The company claims to be the only short-haul, low-fare, high-frequency, point-to-point carrier in the United States (Southwest Airlines 2001a).

Southwest has a strong reputation for keeping fares low. The company's average one-way airfare is about $85 (Southwest Airlines 2001b). The company is also known for driving down prices when it enters new markets. Since Southwest began servicing Albany (New York) International Airport in May 2000, the average fare at Albany has decreased from $170 to $130 and passenger traffic has increased by 30 to 40 percent per month (*Times Union* 2001).

The firm was founded with three jets in 1971 by Rollin King and Herb Kelleher who had several basic principles in mind: get your passengers to their destinations when they want to get there, be on time, offer the lowest possible fares, and make sure they have fun while traveling. Strong and steady growth has occurred over the past 30 years, with Southwest now ranking as the nation's fourth largest airline (Southwest Airlines 2001b).

In 1988, Southwest was the first airline to win the "triple crown" of air travel: best on-time record, best baggage handling, and fewest customer complaints for a one-year period—a feat that no other airline had accomplished for a single month. And the awards have continued since then, including five more triple crowns and recognition from *Fortune* magazine, which ranked Southwest fourth among companies in all industry groups in the magazine's 2001 America's Most Admired Companies list. Numerous mentions of their successful strategies also appear in many books and articles (Southwest Airlines 2001a).

Southwest has also demonstrated that it can keep costs down and not sacrifice innovation. Southwest was the first airline to offer a frequent flyer program that gives credit for the number of trips taken and not the number of miles traveled. The company also initiated many unique customer offerings that are now the industry standard such as senior discounts, fun fares, same-day air freight delivery, and ticketless travel (Southwest Airlines 2001a).

Southwest is well-known for its highly participative corporate culture that encourages innovation, particularly in the area of curbing costs. Having a strike-free company history in an industry plagued by strike threats attests to the company's success at attracting and retaining loyal employees, now numbering more than 32,000, with 82 percent unionized (Southwest Airlines 2001b).

Unconventional policies also abound at Southwest. Company executives are required to perform lower-level job duties on a regular basis. Employees are allowed to wear whatever they want to work and may play practical jokes on each other or sing into the public address system while on the job (*Times Union* 2001).

Plans for future growth by Southwest include adding more points of service on the East Coast and more long-haul flights. The company believes having the lowest operating cost structure in the domestic airline industry will allow it to prosper and offer the lowest and simplest fares, even in a downward economy. A case in point, Southwest was the only major airline that stayed profitable (making both net and operating profits) during the recession of the early 1990s (*Wall Street Journal* 2001). Financial statistics for 2000 show net income of $625.2 million and total operating revenue of $5.6 billion (Southwest Airlines 2001b), giving Southwest solid footing for heading into a new century as the nation's leading and most respected discount airline.

The idea of a cost leadership strategy has not been well-accepted in the healthcare field. Low cost is associated with low quality as mentioned earlier and is often rejected outright as a viable competitive strategy for a healthcare organization. Typical of the thinking on this subject is the work of Pointer (1990) summarized below. He describes the importance to the healthcare organization of determining how to position its products on the value continuum (see Figure 6.3) where

$$\text{Value} = \frac{\text{Quality}}{\text{Cost/Price}}$$

As the graph illustrates, low cost or price is associated with low quality while high cost or price is associated with high quality. Pointer indicates that while "[a]n infinite number of value propositions (cost/price and quality combination on curve OC) are possible . . . in most instances, low cost-price and high quality cannot be achieved simultaneously." Except in rare cases, little demand exists for low-quality healthcare services and therefore, given this construct, for a low-cost strategy.

A few healthcare studies have examined the issue of cost leadership and its application in the field, such as the research of Cleverley and Harvey (1992) and Langabeer (1998). As noted earlier, the findings of the two studies are completely contradictory. The Cleverley and Harvey analysis of 1,000 large urban hospitals found that "[t]he single most important strategy . . . is cost control." Four specific cost strategies were employed effectively by hospitals: length-of-stay management, labor productivity, overhead cost control, and substitution of capital for labor. In contrast, Langabeer studied 100 major teaching hospitals and found that "[T]his research confirms that a low-cost strategy has no influence on financial performance . . . cost leadership was not a viable

**Figure 6.3: Value Proposition Decisions—The Relationship Between Cost/Price and Quality**

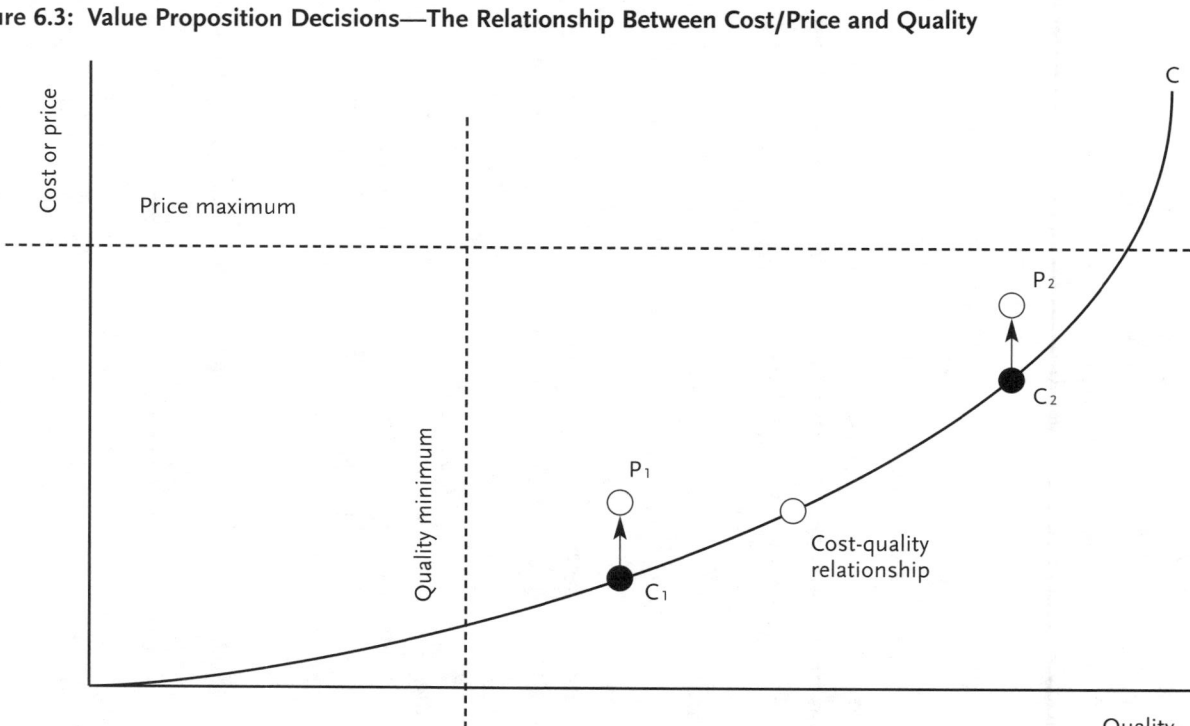

*Source:* Based on concepts from Lele, M. M., and J. N. Sheth. 1987. *The Customer Is Key: Gaining an Unbeatable Advantage Through Customer Satisfaction.* New York: Wiley. From "Offering-Level Strategy Formulation in Health Service Organizations. *Health Care Management Review* 15 (35). Reprinted with permission. Copyright © 1990.

strategy for enhancing financial performance." He goes on to note (Ashmos and McDaniel 1990):

> Low cost strategies have been validated time and again as being the most effective method for competing in stable and predictable environments. The use of a low-cost strategy has not been proven as optimal in an extremely turbulent and rapidly changing marketplace. Indeed, research has identified that hospitals that emphasize low cost focus almost entirely on internal processes and neglect the more important external market conditions.

Luke and Begun (1993) add that "[i]n the 1970s and 1980s, the desire to achieve low cost positions led many hospitals to join multi-hospital systems. . . It is unclear, however, whether that tactic proved successful in helping participating hospitals actually achieve low cost positions. . ."

Duncan, Ginter, and Swayne (1995) note that:

> [A]n industry segment where cost leadership is being used successfully is in the area of long-term care. Long-term-care facilities are a "thin-margin business" in which profit margins range from approximately 1.2 percent to 1.7 percent. In this industry, older facilities are at a competitive disadvantage relative to new facilities. However, long-term-care facilities that have been able to drive costs down while maintaining quality have enjoyed higher margins. In addition, many of these facilities have been upgraded to be more efficient and have instituted tight cost controls. Advertising has been used to keep occupancy above 95 percent, which is often required in the industry to be profitable.

Reimbursement for healthcare services has been a major influence on the acceptability and utility of a cost leadership strategy. Until fairly recently, most reimbursement for healthcare services has guaranteed that costs incurred by providers will be recouped, thus providing no incentive for cost minimization and actually incentivizes the opposite, if anything. With the implementation of prospective payment for inpatient hospital services in the mid-1980s, a new era of reimbursement approaches began. Cost control was given added impetus with the advent of managed care and especially its evolution to capitated payment in the early 1990s. As a result of these developments, cost avoidance began to matter in some sectors of healthcare delivery.

Considerable concern still exists that low cost equates to low quality, although this belief has moderated somewhat as a result of the research findings from general business practices. This research has demonstrated the added cost to business of low quality in terms of rework, repair, loss of customer confidence, and decreased market share.

Gryna (1988) refers to quality costs as the costs associated with preventing, finding, and correcting defective work and notes that these costs can run as high as 20 to 40 percent of sales. In a 1999 interview, Joseph Juran, one of the leading quality theorists who advocated the analysis of quality-related costs as early as 1951, explains the impact of quality on cost (*Fortune Magazine* 1999).

> There's a lot of confusion as to whether quality costs money or whether it saves money. In one sense, quality means the features of some product or service that make people willing to buy it. So it's income-oriented—has an effect on income. Now to produce features, ordinarily you have to invest money. In that sense, higher quality costs more. Quality also means freedom from trouble, freedom from failure. This is cost-oriented. If things fail internally, it costs the company. If they fail externally, it also costs the customer. In these cases, quality costs less.

Similar analyses and implications for healthcare organizations have begun to appear in the healthcare literature. Teisberg, Porter, and Brown (1994) attempt to explain the odd role of quality and costs in the United States healthcare system.

Prices remain high even when there is excess capacity. Technologies remain expensive even when they are widely used. Hospitals and physicians remain in business even when they charge higher prices for equal quality or fail to provide high-quality service. Until recently, incentives existed only for innovations that raised costs or increased quality regardless of cost.

Studies do reveal that better quality care is often lower in cost due to the efficiency of experienced medical teams, fewer complications, and better long-term outcomes. Also, some signs indicate that payers are trying to find approaches for reducing costs, not just denying claims. The Prudential Company estimated that it saved more than 20 percent in costs through a program that directed bone-marrow transplant patients to high-quality providers that were screened on criteria such as facilities, staff, credentials, processes, and past outcomes (Teisberg, Porter, and Brown 1994).

## HEALTHCARE COST LEADERSHIP CASE STUDIES

Despite the lack of clear benefit of the cost-leadership strategy among healthcare providers, some organizations have successfully used this approach to distinguish themselves.

### Aultman Health Foundation

Aultman Health Foundation, in Canton, Ohio, is well-respected in the healthcare industry as a strong and vital independent healthcare network that has made quality, cost-efficiency, and local control the hallmarks of its patient care services. The foundation includes Aultman Hospital, founded in 1892, which has grown to consist of 682 beds, including 18 beds in a Level III neonatal intensive care unit, 48 beds for newborns, 27 rehabilitation beds, and

30 beds licensed for skilled nursing. Aultman Health Foundation also owns Aultman Home Medical Supply Company; AultCare, a 16-year-old managed care company; and Prime Time Health Plan, a Medicare managed care plan (Powell 2000a).

The hospital's active medical staff of 650 physicians has one of the highest board certification rates in Ohio. Major programs for the hospital include oncology, cardiology, orthopedics, emergency and trauma medicine, maternal/child services, and neurosurgery (Aultman Hospital 2001a). The hospital also operates four outpatient satellite facilities that offer a wide range of services (Aultman Hospital 2001b).

Aultman Hospital is the largest medical facility in the five-county region it serves and the last independent hospital in a region where most other providers have joined the Cleveland Clinic Foundation or University Hospitals Health System (Powell 2000a). Instead of sacrificing local control, Aultman convinced several smaller community hospitals to join its loosely aligned network. Participating hospitals and their affiliated physicians are not required to refer patients to Aultman, but a definite shift in referral patterns has occurred. In return, the smaller hospitals have the advantage of being affiliated with an independent, community-oriented powerhouse. For example, Alliance Hospital in Alliance, Ohio, has formed a real estate partnership with Aultman to build a new main hospital campus (Powell 2000b).

*Key Strategies*

This "do-it-yourself, keep-it-local" attitude is demonstrated throughout many of the organization's key strategies—from refusing to sign contracts with outside managed care companies to handling construction projects with a team of inhouse engineers (Powell 2000b). Remaining independent has also enabled Aultman to employ a number of innovative strategies aimed at increasing efficiencies, sustaining high quality, and controlling costs. The organization implemented one of the first and largest robotized hospital laboratories in the country and focused on developing a more efficient materials management program in the 1980s, long before other hospitals followed suit. To attract patients from other managed care plans, Aultman initiated a program that allowed the hospital to waive out-of-network copayment on a case-by-case basis.

As many hospitals have suffered drastic repercussions from cutbacks in payments from insurers and the government, Aultman has kept operating margins on the plus side (about 5 to 7 percent annually) while aggressively adding new programs and services, such as its Level III nursery and Level II trauma unit. According to an HCIA Sachs report, Aultman's average charge per Medicare patient discharged is $6,791, less than half the amount charged by nearby Akron, Ohio, hospitals (Powell 2000b).

In December 2000, Aultman was recognized as one of the nation's top hospitals for the third consecutive year, receiving the HCIA-Sachs National Benchmarks for Success award. The award is based on objective, quantitative performance data. The top 100 hospitals on the list exhibited more than three times the profitability of all other hospitals studied (8.7 percent total profit margin), despite experiencing an increasingly acute patient population, use of more expensive equipment, and lower Medicare reimbursement. If all the hospitals in the United States performed at this level, hospital expenses nationally would decline $12 billion per year. The top hospitals also exhibited superior performance in clinical quality measures, showing fewer complications and inpatient deaths (Aultman Hospital 2000).

Aultman's recognition for top-notch care, reputation for maintaining some of the lowest prices in its region, and skill at forcing competitors to match Aultman charges should serve it well as continuing constraints on reimbursement are forecast for providers.

## Concentra Operating Corporation

Concentra Operating Corporation describes itself as the comprehensive outsource solution for containing healthcare and disability costs. Its mission appears boldly on the corporation's web site: "In recent years, the annual cost of work related injuries to employers has risen to more than $105 billion in the United States. At Concentra our mission is to cut that cost." By providing comprehensive, integrated services, the corporation aims to cut costs in occupational healthcare on a broad scale and at every stage for its clients, which include 3,900 insurance carriers and third-party administrators and more than 130,000 employers in the United States and Canada (Concentra Operating Corporation 2001a). Concentra claims that as an outsourcer of critical functions that companies would otherwise have to handle internally, it can provide a full range of services at substantially lower cost than clients would incur through internal sources (Concentra 2001a).

### Health Services

The corporation's services are divided into three segments. The Health Services segment, operating 224 occupational healthcare facilities in 69 markets across 32 states, provides specialized injury and occupational health services to employers (Concentra Operating Corporation 2001b). The centers handle more than a half million workplace injuries annually, accounting for more than five million visits to its centers each year (Concentra Operating Corporation 2001a). This segment also offers noninjury employment-related services such as physical examinations, substance abuse testing, return-to-work evaluations, and other related programs (Concentra Operating Corporation 2001b).

Concentra's occupational health centers have been able to reduce time lost from work by an average of more than 65 percent by facilitating and providing more immediate response and treatment of injuries. Workers' compensation costs for employers using Concentra's services are typically reduced 10 to 60 percent. By using a system of best practices, Concentra ensures that its customers receive fast turnaround times and high-quality care. The centers are equipped with on-site pharmacies and physical therapy services to allow injured workers the convenience of medical attention under one roof.

In addition to the health centers, Concentra's Health Services segment operates an extensive preferred provider organization (PPO) with about 222,000 providers and more than 3,100 hospitals in all 50 states. PPO providers have agreed to a prenegotiated pricing structure that is significantly lower for patients referred through Concentra. In 2000, the Health Services segment reported revenues of $400 million, accounting for about 53 percent of the corporation's total revenues of $752 million (Concentra Operating Corporation 2001c).

### Network Services

The Network Services segment handles the review and repricing of provider bills and is compensated based on the degree to which Concentra achieves savings for its clients. In 2000, this segment achieved $162 million in revenue.

### Care Management Services

The third segment, Care Management, includes the corporations' services that attempt to curtail the costs of workers' compensation and auto claims through case management, medical examinations, and utilization management (Concentra Operating Corporation 2001b). About 60 percent of the almost $100 billion spent annually on workers' compensation costs come from the cost of replacement wages and legal costs to the employers. Concentra attempts to reduce excessive and unnecessary costs through early intervention and better communication with injured employees. Revenues for Concentra's Care Management segment in 2000 were reported at $190 million (Concentra Operating Corporation 2001a).

Financially, Concentra is exhibiting strong performance. Second quarter results for 2001 indicated revenue of $211,924,000, an increase of 12 percent over the previous year (Concentra Operating Corporation 2001d). This performance follows a period of stellar growth for the corporation, from $305 million in revenues in 1995 to more than $752 million in 2000. During this period, Concentra's employee base has more than doubled to 8,800 and assets have grown from $189 million in 1995 to $657 million in 2000.

Future plans include expansion of its network of occupational health centers, particularly in the Northeast (Concentra Operating Corporation 2001c). But the key strategy for Concentra will remain "to provide focused and cost-effective assistance in controlling rising healthcare costs" (Concentra Operating Corporation 2001a).

## CONCLUSION

Cost leadership is the only competitive strategy discussed in this book that has been broadly successful in the general business community and essentially unsuccessful in healthcare. As a result, numerous for-profit companies outside of healthcare are reaping the rewards of this strategy and few within healthcare, particularly in the not-for-profit sector. This situation is hardly surprising given the historic lack of price competition and regulated reimbursement in healthcare delivery. However, as healthcare continues to deregulate and price competition becomes more commonplace in the future, cost leadership may emerge as one of the critical competitive strategies for healthcare organizations.

# REFERENCES

Ashmos, D. P. and R. R. McDaniel, Jr. 1990. "Physician Participation in Hospital Decision Making: The Effect of Hospital Strategy and Decision Content." *Health Services Research* 26 (3): 375–401.

Aultman Hospital. 2000. "Aultman Hospital Named One of Nation's 100 Top Hospitals for Third Consecutive Year." [Online article retrieval 7/17/01]. http://www.aultman.com/new/press_view.asp?pid=22.

————. 2001a. "About Us." [Online article retrieval 7/17/01]. http://www.aultman.com/aboutus/aboutus.asp.

————. 2001b. "Satellite Facilities." [Online article retrieval 7/17/01]. http://www.aultman.com/aultman_hosp/satellite.html.

Careerbuilder Network. 2001. "The Vanguard Group." [Online article retrieval 8/26/01]. http://job9.cbdr.com/Scripts/CGIHndlr.exe/TEM=tboProfileDisplay.nst/S1=820917.

Cleverley, W. O., and R. K. Harvey. 1992. "Competitive Strategy for Successful Hospital Management." *Hospital and Health Services Administration* 37 (1): 53–69.

Concentra Operating Corporation. 2001a. "Concentra." [Online retrieval 8/27/01]. www.concentra.com.

————. 2001b. "Concentra Operating Corporation Announces Changes in Business Segment Reporting." [Online article retrieval 7/17/01]. http://www.concentramc.com/press_032701.htm.

————. 2001c. "Concentra Health Services Acquires Industrial Health Care Company." [Online article retrieval 7/17/01]. http://www.concentramc.com/press_030501.htm.

————. 2001d. "Concentra Operating Corporation Reports Second Quarter Results." [Online article retrieval 8/27/01]. http://www.concentra.com/2q2001_pr.htm.

Duncan, W. J. , P. M. Ginter, and L. E. Swayne. 1995. *Strategic Management of Health Care Organizations,* 2nd edition. Boston: Blackwell Business.

East Carolina University School of Business. 2000. Course materials: "Strategy and Competitive Advantage." [Online retrieval 1/7/2000]. www.business.ecu.edu/users/simerlyr/PPT2862.htm.

*Fortune Magazine.* 1999. "A Conversation with Joseph Juran: Toward the Century of Quality." January 11, 1999. [Online article retrieval 8/24/01]. http://www.csom.umn.edu/wwwpages/juran/fortune.htm.

Grant, R. M. 1991. *Contemporary Strategy Analysis: Concepts, Techniques, Applications*. Boston: Blackwell Publishing.

Gryna, G. M. 1988. "Quality Costs." In *Juran's Quality Control Handbook*, 4th edition, edited by J. M. Juran and F. M. Gryna. New York: McGraw-Hill.

Hoovers. 2001a. "The Vanguard Group, Inc." [Online article retrieval 8/26/01]. http://www.hoovers.com/co/capsule/1,02163,43321,00.html.

————. 2001b. "Southwest Airlines Company." [Online article retrieval 7/17/01]. http://www.hoovers.com/co/capsule/7/0,2163,11377,00.html.

Langabeer, J. 1998. "Competitive Strategy in Turbulent Healthcare Markets: An Analysis of Financially Effective Teaching Hospitals." *Journal of Healthcare Management* 43 (6): 512–25.

Luke, R. D. and J. W. Begun. 1993. "Strategy Making in Health Care Organizations." In *Health Care Management: Organization Design and Behavior*, 3rd edition, edited by S. Shortell and A. Kaluzny. Albany, NY: Delmar.

Pointer, D. D. 1990. "Offering-Level Strategy Formulation in Health Service Organizations. *Health Care Management Review* 15 (3): 11–19.

Porter, M. E. 1985. *Competitive Advantage: Creating and Sustaining Superior Performance*. New York: Simon and Schuster Trade.

————. 1996. "What is Strategy?" *Harvard Business Review* November/December: 62, 64, 70,73.

————. 1980. *Competitive Strategy: Techniques for Analyzing Industries and Competitors*. New York: The Free Press, a division of Macmillan, Inc.

Powell, C. 2000a. "Leader of Aultman to Retire." *Akron Beacon Journal,* June 15. [Online article retrieval 8/27/01]. http://www.ohio.com/bj/news/2000/June/15/docs/021269.htm.

————. 2000b. "In Charge of Its Future." *Akron Beacon Journal,* December 17. [Online article retrieval 8/27/01]. http://www.ohio.com/bj/news/2000/December/17/docs/013494.htm.

Southwest Airlines. 2001a. "We Weren't Airborne Yesterday." [Online article retrieval 8/26/01]. http://www.iflyswa.com/about_swa/airborne.html.

————. 2001b. "Southwest Airlines Fact Sheet." [Online article retrieval 8/26/01]. http://www.iflyswa.com/about_swa/press/factsheet.html.

Teisberg, E. O, M. E. Porter, and G. B. Brown. 1994. "Making Competition in Health Care Work." *Harvard Business Review* July/August: 131–41.

*Times Union.* 2001. "Southwest Airlines Is Ready to Expand Service." June 22. [Online article retrieval 7/17/01]. www.timesunion.com.

Vanguard Group. 2001a. "About Vanguard: A Unique Corporate Structure." [Online article retrieval 7/17/01]. http://www.vanguard.com/about/1_3_1.html.

———. 2001b. "About Vanguard: Chairman's Welcome." [Online article retrieval 8/26/01]. http://www.vanguard.com/about/1_1.html.

———. 2001c. "Leading the Way: A Short History of The Vanguard Group." [Online article retrieval 7/17/01]. http://www.vanguard.com/about/1_5.html.

Wall Street Journal. 2001. "Southwest Airlines VP James Parker Talks to the Wall Street Transcript." May 8. [Online article retrieval 8/26/01]. http://www.prnewswire.com/cgi-bin/micro_stories.pl?ACC.../001488536&EDATE=May+8,+2000.

# CHAPTER 7

# Differentiation

## INTRODUCTION

DIFFERENTIATION IS THE third (niching and cost leadership being the other two) of the three traditional strategies used by firms to gain competitive advantage. Differentiation has been a popular strategy among U.S. consumer products companies. While it has also been employed by healthcare organizations, it is now being used with more frequency, often through projects such as centers of excellence.

This chapter examines product, quality, and service differentiation theory and applicability, including case studies of companies outside the healthcare field as well as healthcare organizations.

## DIFFERENTIATION DEFINED

According to Porter (1985), "[a] firm differentiates itself from its competitors if it can be unique at something that is valuable to buyers." Grant (1991) states that "[d]ifferentiation advantage occurs when a firm is able to obtain from its differentiation a price premium in the market that exceeds the cost of providing the differentiation."

Differentiation is especially prevalent in U.S. industry among consumer products firms. Relatively similar products possess or are perceived by consumers to have differences that distinguish them from other products of their type. Differentiation is also common among firms offering services.

In healthcare delivery, differentiation is a competitive strategy with a long history, but it is just beginning to be used now with some frequency. Centers of excellence, branding, and the less well developed attempts to offer service excellence or quality excellence represent efforts that healthcare providers are starting to employ in this area.

Three general types of differentiation will be profiled and described in this chapter: product, quality, and service. Although there are similarities and overlaps among the three types, the main characteristics and differences are as follows:

1. *Product*. Differences in the features of the product (or in the case of most healthcare providers, the nature of the service offered) are the focus here. Some potential differences include comprehensiveness, advanced technology, and staffing mix.
2. *Quality*. Differences in the actual outcomes, "production process," or structure of care delivery comprise quality differentiation. Some potential differences include lower morbidity or mortality, significantly improved quality of life after treatment, outstanding Joint Commission on Accreditation of Healthcare Organizations scores, and a high proportion of board-certified physicians.
3. *Service*. Providing exceptional service should be a goal for organizations in the service part of the economy. Some potential differences that healthcare organizations exhibit include very high customer satisfaction scores, rapid outpatient treatment, convenient locations for receiving service, and extended hours of service.

## ADVANTAGES OF DIFFERENTIATION

What is the nature of the competitive advantages that a differentiation strategy offers? Five principal advantages may accrue to the organization:

1. *Engenders brand loyalty.* Buyers develop loyalty to the brand they prefer. Brand loyalty is especially prevalent in the consumer products industries but is increasingly being applied in service industries (e.g., Federal Express, Amazon, and Nordstrom).
2. *Reduces buyer leverage.* Bargaining power is reduced, especially for large buyers who otherwise might have much more transaction leverage, since other similar products are far less appealing.
3. *Reduces supplier leverage.* Suppliers, especially large suppliers, will have less leverage with the organization since it stands out from others and suppliers will be concerned about losing an important and potentially ever more significant customer.
4. *Creates barriers to entry.* Loyal buyers serve as a deterrent to other organizations seeking to enter or considering entrance to the field.
5. *Offsets threats of substitutes.* Substitute products (or services) are always a concern for an organization; however, customers' attachment to the differentiating attributes at least partially offsets the ability of substitutes to successfully draw the organization's customers.

Figure 7.1 summarizes the typical situations in which a differentiation strategy works best as well as the major pitfalls of a differentiation strategy. Figure 7.2 identifies some of the major product differentiation approaches and American businesses that typify the successful deployment of each approach. Figure 7.2 also includes

**Figure 7.1: When Differentiation Is Likely and Unlikely to Succeed**

When a Differentiation Strategy Works Best
- Differences perceived by buyers to have value
- Diverse needs and uses of an item
- Differentiation approach used by few rivals

Pitfalls of a Differentiation Strategy
- Trying to differentiate on a feature buyers do not perceive as lowering their cost or enhancing their well-being
- Over-differentiating such that product features exceed buyers' needs
- Charging a price premium that buyers perceive is too high
- Ignoring need to signal value, depending only on "real" bases of differentiation
- Not identifying what buyers will consider as value

*Source:* Reprinted, with permission, from "Strategy and Competitive Advantage," East Carolina University School of Business course material. Copyright © 2000.

guidelines about where to look for differentiation opportunities in the organization. With this information as a starting point, we turn to a more detailed examination of the mechanics of differentiation and a review of the general business literature on the effectiveness of this competitive strategy.

## DIFFERENTIATION THEORY AND APPLICABILITY IN INDUSTRY

According to Porter (1985), "[d]ifferentiation stems from uniquely creating buyer value" that leads to lower cost for the buyer, higher performance, or both. He also states that "[d]ifferentiation cannot be understood by viewing the firm in aggregate, but stems from the specific activities the firm performs and how they affect the buyer."

**Figure 7.2: The "How-To" of Differentiation**

Approaches to Differentiation
- Different taste—Dr. Pepper
- Superior service—Federal Express
- Spare parts availability—Caterpillar
- Engineering design and performance—Mercedes
- Prestige—Rolex
- Quality—Honda automobiles
- Top-of-the-line image—Ralph Lauren
- Technological leadership—3M
- Unconditional satisfaction—L. L. Bean and Lands' End

Where to Look for Differentiation Opportunities
- Purchasing and procurement activities
- Product-oriented R & D activities
- Production process–oriented R & D activities
- Manufacturing activities
- Outbound logistics and distribution activities
- Marketing, sales, and service activities

*Note:* R & D = research and development.
*Source:* Reprinted, with permission, from "Strategy and Competitive Advantage," East Carolina University School of Business course material. Copyright © 2000.

Porter (1985) also notes that most organizations have a narrow perspective of differentiation:

> Firms view the potential sources of differentiation too narrowly. They see differentiation in terms of the physical product or marketing practices, rather than potentially arising anywhere in the value chain. Firms are also often different but not differentiated, because they pursue forms of uniqueness that buyers do not value. Differentiators also frequently pay insufficient attention to the cost of differentiation, or to the sustainability of differentiation once achieved.

Sources of differentiation in the value chain are illustrated in Figure 7.3.

Grant (1991) describes how differentiation must be implemented:

> Successful differentiation involves matching customers' demand for differentiation with the firm's capacity to supply differentiation. . . . Analyzing customer demand enables us to determine the potential for differentiation to appeal to customers, their willingness to pay for differentiation, and the most promising position in relation to competitors.

In the following pages, we will examine the opportunities for differentiation on the demand side first and then discuss the supply side.

## DIFFERENTIATION AND DEMAND

Figure 7.4 presents a framework for achieving a more complete understanding of why customers buy a product or service. It is critical to break down customer buying patterns and needs in this way to determine what the basic customer needs are that must be met. Two aspects of this analysis are of particular importance:

1. *Product attributes and positioning.* Since essentially all products and services serve multiple customer needs, approaches need to be applied to determine what consumer preferences really are in relation to each product attribute. This approach then guides new product positioning and existing product repositioning.
2. *Social and psychological factors.* As Grant (1991) notes, few goods or services are purchased for survival. Most consumer spending reflects social goals and values as they relate to finding community with others, establishing an identity, and making sense of what is happening in the world. If organizations want

# Figure 7.3: Representative Sources of Differentiation in the Value Chain

| | | Top Management Support in Selling<br>Facilities that Enhance the Firm's Image<br>Superior Management Information System | | | | MARGIN |
|---|---|---|---|---|---|---|
| **FIRM INFRASTRUCTURE** | | | | | | |
| **HUMAN RESOURCE MANAGEMENT** | | • Stable Workforce Polices<br>• Quality of Work Life Programs<br>• Programs to Attract the Best Scientists and Engineers | | • Sales Incentives to Retain Best Salespersons<br>• Recruiting Better Qualified Sales and Service Personnel | | • Extensive Training of Service Technician |
| **TECHNOLOGY DEVELOPMENT** | | • Unique Product Features<br>• Rapid Model Introductions<br>• Unique Production Process or Machines<br>• Automated Inspection Procedures | • Unique Vehicle Scheduling Software<br>• Special Purpose Vehicles or Containers | • Applications Engineering Support<br>• Superior Media Research<br>• Most Rapid Quotations for Tailored Models | | • Advanced Servicing Techniques |
| **PROCUREMENT** | | • Highest Quality Raw Materials<br>• Highest Quality Components | • Best Located Warehouses<br>• Transportation Suppliers that Minimize Damage | • Most Desirable Media Placements<br>• Product Positioning and Image | | • High Quality Replacement Parts |
| | • Superior Material Handling & Sorting Technology<br>• Proprietary Quality Assurance Equipment | • Tight Conformance to Specifications<br>• Attractive Product Appearance<br>• Responsiveness to Specification Changes<br>• Low Defect Rates<br>• Short Time to Manufacture | • Rapid and Timely Delivery<br>• Accurate and Responsive Order Processing<br>• Handling that Minimizes Damage | • High Advertising Level and Quality<br>• High Sales Force Coverage and Quality<br>• Personal Relationships with Channels or Buyers<br>• Superior Technical Literature and Other Sales Aids<br>• Most Extensive Promotion<br>• Most Extensive Credit to Buyers or Channels | | • Rapid Installation<br>• High Service Quality<br>• Complete Field Stocking of Replacement Parts<br>• Wide Service Coverage<br>• Extensive Buyer Training |
| | • Most Reliable Transportation for Inbound Deliveries<br>• Handling of Inputs that Minimizes Damage or Degradation<br>• Timeliness of Supply to the Manufacturing Process | | | | | |
| | **INBOUND LOGISTICS** | **OPERATIONS** | **OUTBOUND LOGISTICS** | **MARKETING & SALES** | | **SERVICE** |

MARGIN

*Source:* Reprinted with the permission of The Free Press, a division of Simon & Schuster, Inc., from COMPETITIVE STRATEGY: *Techniques for Analyzing Industries and Competitors* by Michael E. Porter. Copyright © 1980, 1998 by The Free Press.

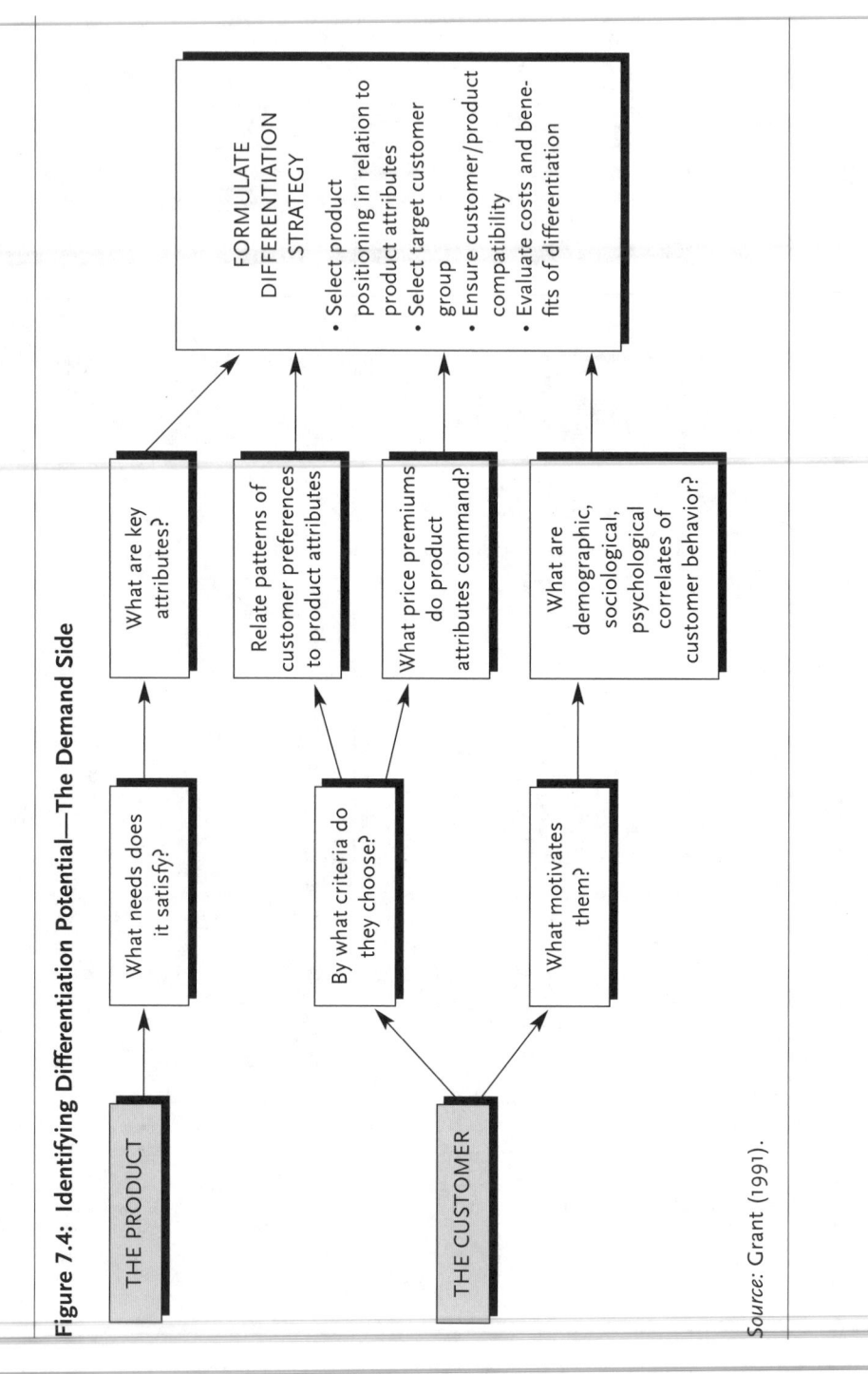

*Source:* Grant (1991).

to employ differentiation as a key strategy, they must understand customer demand and evaluate the lifestyles, personalities, and social groupings of the customers.

## DIFFERENTIATION AND SUPPLY

Figure 7.5 presents a framework for obtaining a complete understanding of an organization's potential to supply differentiation. Four aspects of the supply side of differentiation, the drivers of uniqueness, product integrity, signaling and reputation, and the costs of differentiation, are especially critical.

### The Drivers of Uniqueness

As noted previously, the ability to create uniqueness is not limited to one or two aspects of the organization's product or processes, but is broadly available. According to Porter (1985), the principal areas in which uniqueness may be derived include:

- Product features and product performance
- Complementary services (e.g., credit, delivery, repair)
- Intensity of marketing activities (e.g., rate of advertising spending)
- Technology embodied in design and manufacture
- The quality of purchased inputs
- Procedures influencing the conduct of each activity (e.g., rigor of quality control, service procedures, frequency of sales visits to a customer)
- The skill and experience of employees
- Location (e.g., with retail stores)
- The degree of vertical integration (which influences a firm's ability to control inputs and intermediate processes).

**Figure 7.5: Assessing the Value Chain to Identify Differentiation Potential on the Supply Side**

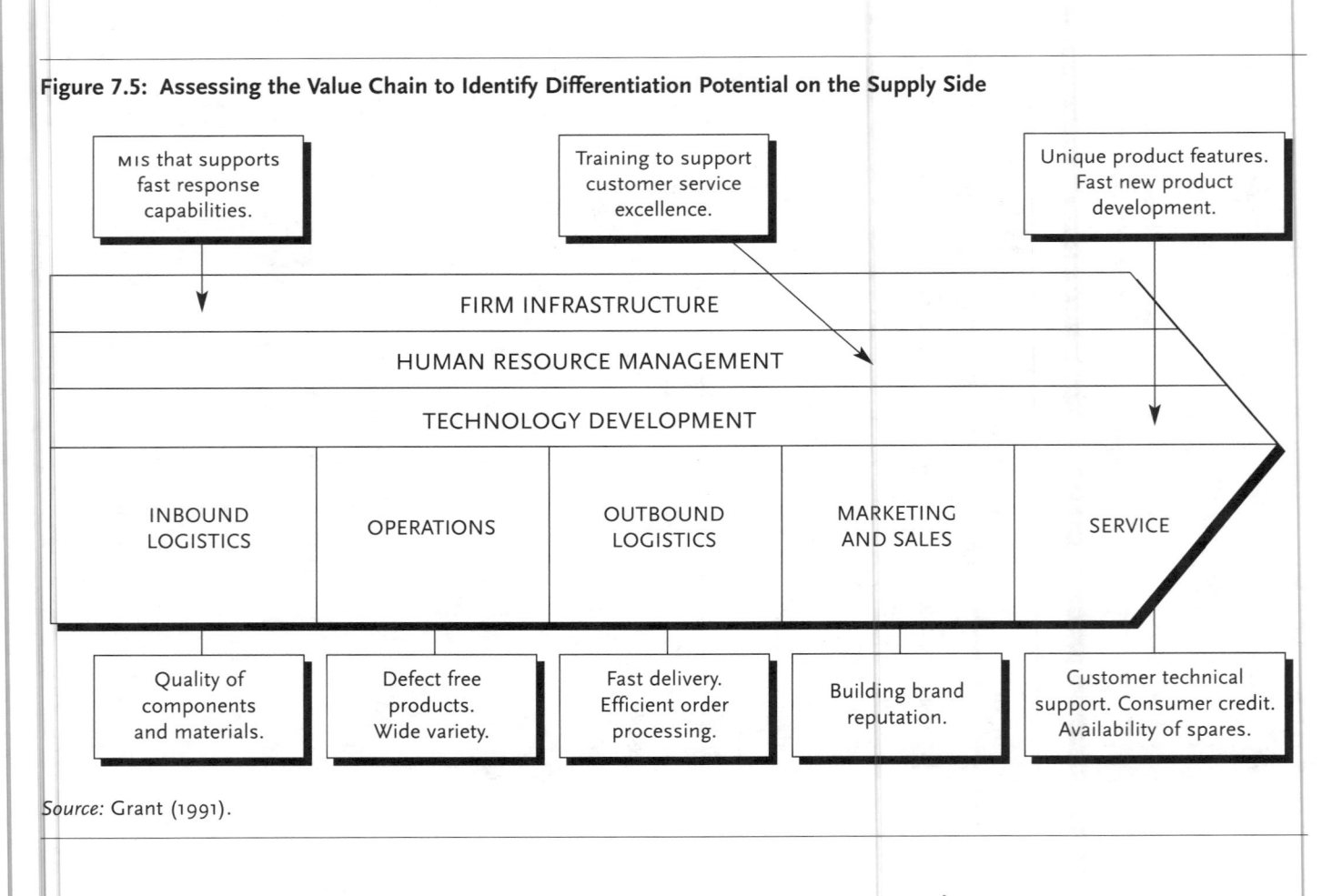

## Product Integrity

According to Grant (1991), product integrity focuses on the consistency of the organization's differentiation. Do the internal activities and processes lead to a coherent product or service and do the external activities and processes support the product or service's structure and function and present a consistent image to the marketplace? According to Grant (1991), this aspect "[i]s especially important to organizations seeking image differentiation where the credibility of the image depends critically on the consistency of the image presented."

## Signaling and Reputation

Grant (1991) also notes that "[d]ifferentiation is only effective if it is communicated to customers." The term *signaling* refers to conveying the differentiation character to the customer. Signaling and reputation are most important where quality is too difficult to determine even after purchase. Having a strong reputation obviously reinforces the strength of the signal conveyed by the firm.

## The Costs of Differentiation

A differentiation strategy can be costly. As a result, Porter (1985) believes organizations should:

1. "Exploit all sources of differentiation that are not costly
2. Minimize the cost of differentiation by controlling cost drivers, particularly the cost of signaling
3. Emphasize forms of differentiation where the firm has a sustainable cost advantage in differentiating
4. Reduce cost in activities that do not affect buyer value."

## SUMMARY OF RESEARCH IMPLICATIONS FOR A DIFFERENTIATION STRATEGY

Porter (1985) notes,

> [t]he sustainability of differentiation depends on two things, its continued perceived value to buyers and the lack of imitation by competitors. There is an ever-present risk that buyers' needs or perceptions will change, eliminating the value of a particular form of differentiation. Competitors may also imitate the firm's strategy or leapfrog the bases of differentiation a firm has chosen. . . To be sustainable, differentiation must be based on sources where there are mobility barriers to competitors replicating them.

The following factors increase the likelihood of sustainability:

- *Sources of uniqueness involve barriers*. Proprietary learning, linkages, interrelationships, and first-mover advantages are among the most significant barriers.
- *Cost advantage in differentiating*. The existence of cost advantage in performing the differentiating activities.
- *Multiple sources of differentiation*. The more sources of uniqueness, the more difficult it will be to overcome them in the aggregate.
- *Creation of switching costs at the time of differentiation*. Activities that make a firm unique often result in higher switching costs for the buyer when the firm has structured its activities to exploit its uniqueness.

Finally, some of the common mistakes that firms make in employing differentiation strategies include:

- *Emphasizing uniqueness that is not valuable*. Uniqueness leads to differentiation only if it lowers buyer cost or raises buyer performance.

- *Differentiating too much.* Excessive differentiation (e.g., product quality or service levels higher than buyers' needs) may be too costly or just miss the mark.
- *Extracting too big a price premium.* Attempting to extract a price premium in excess of the value of differentiation to the buyer will not yield commensurate differentiation benefits.
- *Failing to signal value.* As noted earlier, failing to communicate adequately the differentiation's value to customers may also result in an inadequate yield from differentiation.
- *Not knowing the cost of differentiation.* Failure to understand costs can lead to spending more on differentiation than the price premium it yields or not realizing the potential to reduce the cost of differentiation.
- *Focusing on the product instead of the whole value chain.* A common mistake is to focus too narrowly on the physical product (or characteristics of the service provided) versus looking for differentiating possibilities throughout the entire production, marketing, and distribution process.
- *Failing to recognize buyer segments.* Ignoring the existence or needs of segments within a buyer group leaves the firm vulnerable to a niche strategy by a competitor.

General, nonacademic business literature is replete with popular books on the value of differentiation. In the past 10 to 15 years, these books have emphasized customer service over technical quality or product attributes, probably reflecting the evolution of the U.S. economy to a more service-oriented economy (versus manufacturing) and the importance of excellent service in such a structure.

Popular works such as Tom Peters' *In Search of Excellence: Lessons from America's Best Run Companies* and *The Circle of Innovation* and Karl Albrecht's and Ron Zemke's *Service America* and *Service America in the New Economy* generally take the position that a particular aspect of differentiation should be emphasized by all firms, which will lead to certain success. But as the preceding section of this chapter indicates, it is not quite that simple a process.

## CASE STUDIES: PRODUCT, QUALITY, AND SERVICE DIFFERENTIATION

The following examples of notable and successful differentiators provide further insight into how these strategies play out in non-healthcare businesses.

### Product Differentiators: The Coca-Cola Company and 3M

The Coca-Cola Company was one of the nation's first companies to merit the designation of a successful product differentiator. Founded in 1886 with the invention of Coca-Cola® by Dr. John Pemberton, the company is now the largest manufacturer, distributor, and marketer of soft drink concentrates and syrups in the world that are used to produce more than 230 beverage brands. Every second of every day, an average of 13,000 of the company's beverages are consumed (The Coca-Cola Company 2001).

But it is the unique carbonated Coca-Cola® beverage that launched the company and will remain the core brand driving worldwide growth for the company as it seeks to establish more global brands, such as diet Coke, Fanta, and Sprite. According to Douglas N. Daft, Coca-Cola chairman and chief executive officer, "The future of The Coca-Cola Company rests with the power and promise of our core brand—Coca Cola®. Brand Coca Cola® is driving our growth around the world" (The Coca-Cola Company 2000). In 2000, approximately 62 percent of the company's total gallon sales were products carrying the Coca-Cola® or Coke® trademark (Yahoo!Finance 2001a).

Minnesota Mining and Manufacturing Company (3M) is also renowned for its product differentiation and innovation. Unlike The Coca-Cola Company, which relies heavily on one brand, 3M has six operating segments engaged in the research, manufacturing, and marketing of industrial, graphics and safety, healthcare, consumer and office, electro and communications, and specialty material products. The common theme among these products is the use of 3M's original cutting-edge technology related to coatings, bondings, and abrasives—what 3M refers to as technical differentiation.

Among 3M products are many popular brands that were unique when introduced to the consumer market and are now part of the American lexicon, such as Scotchgard, Post-It Notes, Scotch tape, and Scotch-Brite (Hoovers 2001a). But 3M is not complacent about resting on the success of its established products. In 2000, nearly 35 percent of total sales ($5.6 billion) was generated from products introduced during the past four years (3M 2000).

3M actively pursues product innovation throughout the company. The company sponsors a "boot camp" program that enables ambitious 3M employees to form their own companies. These companies are supported by 3M through business arrangements, with the possibility of licensing the spinoff's technology (*Austin Business Journal* 1998). To ensure that 3M hires employees with an innovative spirit, the company assembled a team of experts to research and develop a profile of innovators that can be used during the hiring process (University of Minnesota 2001).

## Quality Differentiators: The Maytag Corporation and Sony Corporation

With more than 100 years in business as one of the leading home and commercial appliance manufacturers, the Maytag Corporation has differentiated itself from competitors with its high-quality products, which it defines in appliance terms as durability and reliability (Maytag Corporation 2000). This image has been galvanized by its decades-old advertising campaign (whose images still appear on Maytag's web site) that featured a lonely Maytag repairman.

The $4.2 billion company is among the top three major appliance manufacturers in North America, along with Whirlpool and General Electric. In addition to the Maytag name, its products are sold under the brands Amana, Jenn-Air, Magic Chef, Admiral, and Dynasty. Maytag also owns the Hoover brand, considered the floor-care brand with the highest consumer recognition and buying preference. In addition, Maytag supplies cooking appliances for commercial businesses, under brand names such as Blodgett, and is a major supplier of vending machines under the Dixie-Narco brand (Maytag Corporation 2001).

To achieve its mission of superior quality, Maytag's core business strategies are innovation and research and development (Maytag Corporation 2000). Maytag has also been ambitious in buying out competitors under the rationale that it is reinforcing and extending its premium brand strategy, as demonstrated by its 2000 acquisition of Amana. The Amana buyout was driven in large part to acquire Amana's expertise in refrigeration—historically Maytag's weakest product category. But industry analysts have questioned whether the acquisitions, particularly of lower-priced brands such as Magic Chef and Admiral, have strengthened the corporation or weakened it by diluting the quality Maytag brand.

Despite its detractors, Maytag is the number one consumer brand in washers, dryers, and dishwashers, while Jenn-Air is the number one consumer preferred brand in cooking (PR Newswire 2000). Furthermore, leading consumer publications and retail partners frequently cite Maytag brands among the top appliances.

The Sony Corporation is rated the number two consumer electronics firm in the world (after Matsushita), producing semiconductors, DVD players, cameras, stereo systems, computer monitors, flat-screen televisions, and the highly popular PlayStation, a home video game system that is the firm's most profitable product ever.

Sony is also a multimedia giant with assets that include Columbia Tristar (motion pictures and television shows), record labels such as Columbia and Epic, and insurance and finance businesses (Hoovers 2001b).

Founded in 1946 as Tokyo Telecommunications by engineers who had worked on World War II military technology, the company produced the first Japanese tape recorder in 1950 and then sparked a consumer electronics revolution in Japan after purchasing transistor technology licenses from Western Electric. Renamed Sony in 1958 (from *sonus,* Latin for sound) (Sony Corporation 2001a), the company began building an admirable track record for beating the competition to newly emerging markets.

Yet Sony's true differentiation strategy has been its emphasis on quality, a priority emerging from the corporation's commitment to being a leader in transforming the image of Japanese products after World War II. Sony was also dedicated to meeting the demand for high-quality products from university scholars, research laboratories, and other businesses that needed to replace equipment destroyed during the war (Sony Corporation 2001a).

To date, Sony seems to have held true to its quality commitment. In May 2001, for the second year in a row and the fourth time in the last six years, Sony was selected as the best brand according to the Harris Poll's annual survey of best brands.

### Service Differentiators: Nordstrom Inc. and FedEx Corporation

Since 1901 when John Nordstrom used his $13,000 in earnings from the Alaska gold rush to start a small shoe store in Seattle, Nordstrom's central business philosophy has been exceptional customer service (Nordstrom 2001a). As the company grew to be the largest independent shoe chain in the United States and then one of the nation's leading fashion retailers, quality, value, and selection have also emerged as key business principles. But it is the company's overriding commitment to customer service that has truly differentiated Nordstrom and is demonstrated by a devoted customer base.

With 124 stores located in 24 states, Nordstrom has strived to establish a brand identity that does not bring to mind a fashionable outfit or a perfect pair of shoes, but rather is associated with the people who help customers find what they are looking for. According to Nordstrom's annual report, "This person you can picture so vividly represents the very foundation of our company. The essence of our culture. What sets us apart. This, of course is the Nordstrom salesperson" (Nordstrom 2001b).

Recent initiatives by Nordstrom demonstrate its ongoing commitment to excellent service. Currently underway are activities to connect all company resources with the selling floor and placing decision making as close to the customer as possible. Department managers, store managers, and buyers, many of whom started out as sales personnel, have been charged with focusing their time and energy on feedback received from salespeople and customers. Nordstrom believes this approach will ensure that the right mix of merchandise is available and customer needs are being met (Nordstrom 2001b). According to Bruce Nordstrom, president of the company, "It's no secret that Nordstrom's customer service ethic is what built this company's reputation. And after all, without that reputation, we would be just another store" (Nordstrom 2001b).

FedEx Corporation is another company that has distinguished itself in the area of customer service. The corporation consists of five subsidiaries. The Federal Express unit is the world's number one express transport company, which delivers about 3.3 million packages each day. The FedEx Ground unit handles small packages in North America, while FedEx Custom Critical specializes in urgent deliveries. FedEx Freights handles bulk shipments that are less than a full truckload, and customs brokerage services are available through FedEx Trade Networks (Hoovers 2001c). Each company operates independently but competes under the strong FedEx brand to form what the company describes as the "$20 billion market leader in transportation, information, and logistics solutions" (FedEx Corporation 2001).

Since its founding in 1971, the corporation has focused on creating transportation, information, and logistics networks that provide true customer benefits. Its innovations to manage vehicles, people, packages, routes, and weather in real time have led to a highly efficient organization that streamlines customer involvement in the shipping process, particularly through its online processing and tracking system. FedEx's efforts in this area gained national exposure when it was the first company to win the Malcolm Baldrige National Quality award in the service category (FedEx Corporation 2001).

But FedEx is not complacent about its high rankings for customer service. In 2000, the corporation launched an initiative to make customer-related activities more accessible and customer-friendly. This "one-touch" approach includes one toll-free number, one web site, and a single sales force for ground shipping and express services. The company is also moving toward a single account number and invoice for the full range of FedEx services. According to Laurie Tucker, senior vice president of electronic commerce and customer service for Federal Express, "This company has always listened to the customer. Now it's about anticipating the customer. There's no time for incremental improvement" (Fast Company 1999).

## DIFFERENTIATION THEORY AND APPLICABILITY IN HEALTHCARE

An abundance of healthcare literature has been written about differentiation and particularly on various aspects of differentiation in healthcare as a way to achieve competitive advantage. Duncan, Ginter, and Swayne (1995) provide a useful summary of both theory and practice as applied to healthcare:

Differentiation is a strategy to make the product or service different (or appear so in the mind of the buyer) from competitors' products or services. Thus, consumers see the service as unique among a group of similar competing services.

The product or service may be differentiated by emphasizing quality, a high level of service, ease of access, convenience, reputation, and so on. There are a number of ways to differentiate a product or service, but the attributes that are to be viewed as different or unique must be valued by the consumer. Therefore, organizations using differentiation strategies rely on brand loyalty (reputation or image), distinctive products or services, and the lack of good substitutes.

The most common forms of differentiation in the healthcare industry have been based on quality and image. Many acute-care hospitals emphasize and promote quality care as the difference between them and other hospitals in their service area. Similarly, a "high-tech" image is often the basis for differentiation among healthcare organizations. Affiliation with a medical school, performing the most sophisticated procedures, or using the latest (often expensive) technology may promote the image of "the best possible care."

Luke and Begun (1993) add that in service industries such as healthcare, consumption and production generally occur at the same time. "The simultaneity of production and consumption means that consumers come into contact with organizations at many points and levels. Differentiation is therefore far more than a matter of product design; it is a matter of designing the very character of the organization itself."

Pointer (1990) expands on this last concept by noting that service organizations must deal with the challenge of operating in an environment in which customers are an integral and intimate part of the production system as opposed to the manufacturing company that produces a product that is consumed or used by the customer later.

There have been few studies of the impact of a differentiation strategy on the competitiveness of healthcare organizations. Cleverley and Harvey (1992) suggest that "market leaders . . . are expected to benefit from innovation," and their previously referenced study on hospital competitive strategy only addresses the value of differentiation in indirect ways.

Langabeer (1998) did attempt to measure the effectiveness of a product market strategy (i.e., the selection of particular products and demographic or geographic segments to focus on) in his previously referenced study of the competitive strategy used by teaching hospitals. He indicates that "[t]he most viable process for improving margins is through the strategic selection of an appropriate portfolio of products and services to be offered." Nonetheless, the two variables used to represent product market strategy in Langabeer's analysis have negative statistically significant relationships with financial performance. He notes, however, that "the financially successful hospitals were . . . capable of charging higher prices relative to the competition [based on] higher quality, higher perceived value, or other organizational differentiation."

Although their study of health systems and strategy in the late 1980s only touched upon differentiation peripherally, Shortell, Morrison, and Friedman (1990) write that "[t]he winning healthcare corporation of the future . . . will need to differentiate themselves to some extent on quality features—either clinical, or those more closely related to patient access, comfort, convenience, and service."

More recently, Griffith (2000) concludes that "[s]uccess for [integrated health systems] now includes documented performance on at least three dimensions: quality, cost, and patient satisfaction . . . Like Michael Porter's 'sustainable competitive advantage' winning companies, champions [i.e., those systems which perform well on the measures indicated above] will have staying power."

Until the past ten years or so, healthcare quality was assumed to be uniformly high by American providers and patients. Largely driven by the growth in the healthcare delivery system and by the unending and rapidly increasing pace of medical innovations, it was generally believed that Americans had access to the world's best doctors, hospitals, and other healthcare delivery elements. Furthermore, since access was not markedly constrained, except for the uninformed, uninsured, and to a lesser degree, the medically indigent, quality care was perceived to be nearly universally available.

However, the growth of managed care, restrictions on access, media attention, and better information about what really constitutes quality began to transform the American public's view of healthcare quality in the 1990s. Horror stories of managed care companies controlling consumer access to needed healthcare services became commonplace in the media. The early measures of technical quality for healthcare services and providers also became available and were widely publicized by the media. These measures, largely focused on open-heart surgery and overall hospital quality of care, were by no means uniformly excellent. Finally, in the late 1990s, the Institute of Medicine convened an expert panel on healthcare quality. The panel came to a number of conclusions, but most relevant for this text are the following (Chassin, Galvin, and National Roundtable on Health Care Quality 1998):

> The quality of healthcare can be precisely defined and measured with a degree of scientific accuracy comparable with that of most measures used in clinical medicine. Serious and widespread quality problems exist throughout American medicine. These problems, which may be classified as underuse, overuse, or misuse, occur in small and large communities alike, in all parts of the country, and with approximately equal frequency in managed care and fee-for-service systems of care. Very large numbers of Americans are harmed as a direct result. Quality of care is the

problem, not managed care. Current efforts to improve will not succeed unless we undertake a major, systematic effort to overhaul how we deliver healthcare services, educate and train clinicians, and assess and improve quality.

Subsequent media attention focused on the dramatic data revealed in the Institute of Medicine study. The report stated that medical errors by healthcare facilities and practitioners result in the death of between 44,000 and 98,000 patients every year and add as much as $29 billion to Americans' medical bills annually (Hallam 1999). Predictably, these revelations led to various federal proposals for increased government oversight of the healthcare industry and escalating media focus on quality problems in the healthcare system.

To better understand how healthcare consumers view the importance of quality, a telephone survey of approximately 2,000 Americans was carried out by the Henry J. Kaiser Family Foundation, the Agency for Healthcare Policy and Research of the U.S. Department of Health and Human Services, and Princeton Survey Research Associates in 1996. Among the major findings were (Robinson and Brodie 1997):

1. Americans believe that at least to some degree, quality varies among health plans, hospitals, specialists, and physicians;
2. they value quality in their health plan choices over other factors; and
3. they rely on those they trust—their personal physician, family, and friends—for recommendations on health plans and providers.

Regarding point 3, Figure 7.6, based on data from the survey, shows that although at the time of the survey Americans regarded quality information as useful in healthcare decision making, it was not used frequently by the individuals surveyed in their own decision making. Also, Moore and Bopp (1999) report that the survey found only a

**Figure 7.6: Most Think Comparative Information on Quality Is Useful, But Few Have Used It in Their Own Healthcare Decision Making**

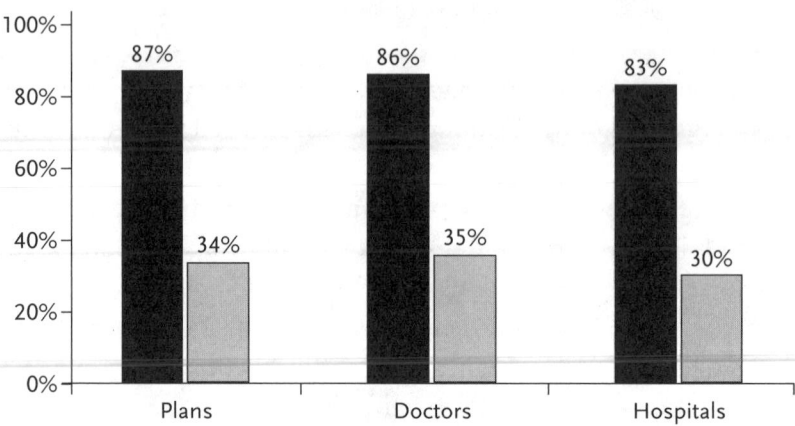

Among those who have seen information comparing quality of plans, doctors, or hospitals who say . . .

- ■ Information would be useful to someone making healthcare decision
- ▢ Personally used information to make healthcare decision

*Source:* Americans as Health Care Consumers: The Role of Quality Information, KFF/AHCPR/PSRA, October 1996 © S. Robinson and M. Brodie: "Understanding the Quality Challenge for Health Consumers: The Kaiser/AHCPR Survey." *Journal of Quality Improvement* 23(5): 239, 1997. Reprinted with permission.

small number of consumers who can recall being exposed to information regarding the quality of healthcare plans, doctors, and hospitals. Only about one out of three consumers recalled having encountered quality-related information in health plans and insurance companies. For doctors the proportion is close to one out of ten and for hospitals the proportion is about one out of five.

In a more recent article, MacStravic (2000) notes that "[q]uality indicators and their publication are some of the fastest growing products in American commerce, and the healthcare industry seems to offer more than its share." He goes on to cite dozens of different publicly available sources of such information and concludes that the diversity of information available renders such information largely useless to the general public. He argues that what is needed is a single "overall quality indicator that could suggest which plans and providers are best."

The increasing availability of information about healthcare quality and the growing interest in this subject among the general public have created a situation in which quality measurement, improvement, and potential use in differentiation are more and more a focus of healthcare delivery organizations today. While, as pointed out above, the indicators available now are often crude, inconsistent, and confusing, all of the activity on this front suggests that progress will be occurring at an even faster rate and quality will certainly be increasingly useful as a point of differentiation in the foreseeable future.

The growing availability of nationally recognized awards for healthcare quality both adds to the interest in this subject and its utility as a differentiation mechanism. Beginning with the Joint Commission on Accreditation of Health Care Organizations' accreditation with commendation in the 1990s, the National Committee for Quality Health Care annual award, the extension of the Baldrige National Quality Program to healthcare in the late 1990s, and the development of the magnet status designation by the American Nurses Association for excellence in nursing, some providers are increasingly able to cite an external source as proof of their distinguished quality.

Finally, Griffith (2000) cites clinical quality as one of eight areas of emphasis for healthcare organizations that will be distinguished, or "champions" as he terms them, in the future. Figure 7.7 lists the critical questions, key measures, common problems, and improvement paths that constitute the approach leading to the development of "championship processes" in this important area.

**Figure 7.7: Designing Championship Processes for Integrated Health Systems**

| Critical Questions | Key Measures | Common Problems | Improvement Path |
|---|---|---|---|
| • Are we achieving optimum outcomes?<br>• Are patients delighted with services?<br>• Are we providing effective prevention? | • Outcomes measures by disease entity<br>• Patient satisfaction data by sites of care<br>• Measures of preventable diseases and prevention programs | • Caregiver denial of outcomes measures<br>• Services too small to operate effectively<br>• Inability to integrate functional services into service lines<br>• Resistance to prevention strategy | • Buyer insistence on outcomes achievement<br>• Continuous improvement teams<br>• Protocols and best practices<br>• Benchmarks and competitor data<br>• Incentives for quality performance |

*Source:* Used with permission from *Journal of Healthcare Management* 45 (1): 25. (Chicago: Health Administration Press, 2000).

With this background information, it should be helpful to highlight a healthcare organization that has been a leader in the quality differentiation movement to achieve a better understanding of how it has evolved as a competitive strategy.

## Quality Differentiator: Johns Hopkins Hospital and Health System

The Johns Hopkins Hospital and Health System is recognized as one of the nation's premier healthcare providers and research institutions. The 1,039-bed hospital, the cornerstone of Johns Hopkins Medicine (which includes the hospital, health system, and school of medicine), has been rated as the nation's top hospital for 11 consecutive years by the *U.S. News & World Report* and was noted in 2000 for exceptional performance in 16 of the 17 specialty rankings by the magazine (Johns Hopkins 2001a).

Founded in 1889 as one of the nation's first teaching hospitals, Hopkins has built a reputation for excellence that is unparalleled in the United States and perhaps the world. Hopkins' clinicians and scientists have been responsible for engendering an entrepreneurial attitude that has led to accelerated medical research (and more federal research funding than any other academic institution in the United States) and set the benchmark for the highest-quality patient care (Worldcare.com 2001). The hospital, health system, and school of medicine are housed on two medical campuses and include numerous outreach programs.

Hopkins' physician-scientist model, with the hospital staffed almost exclusively by full-time faculty physicians, and its ability to transfer research findings to patient care quite rapidly are the foundations of its high-quality medical education, physician training, and clinical care. In the past five years, the school of medicine has formed 12 new companies and entered into hundreds of licensing agreements to streamline the movement of research from the laboratory to the bedside. Its stellar reputation has also spread to a global level, with the hospital's international patient services program now seeing about 7,000 international patients annually (Worldcare.com 2001).

## SERVICE DIFFERENTIATION IN HEALTHCARE

While technical quality and providing distinctive and leading products are certainly important in a service industry like healthcare, nothing is more critical to the customer than service itself. Surveys both in and out of healthcare have demonstrated the value of excellent customer service in building strong customer relationships. Even in healthcare delivery, where an accurate diagnosis and prompt treatment or care would seem to be essential to customer satisfaction, excellent service is most important to consumers.

Figures 7.8 through 7.10 illustrate the importance of good service in satisfying and retaining patients. Figure 7.8 presents data that show the frequency with which problems (and these are primarily, but not exclusively, service problems) occur in selected provider settings and the impact of the number of problems experienced on patient satisfaction. It is surprising that patients report so many problems in each episode of care, but not surprising how patient satisfaction declines precipitously with increasing numbers of mishaps.

Figures 7.9 and 7.10 extend this notion further. Figure 7.9 indicates that even for those with a good relationship with a hospital, nearly three-quarters would switch to another hospital for a better product or service. The figures also demonstrate that service levels are not terribly high in healthcare, so there is a strong desire among consumers to seek providers who can offer better service. Figure 7.10 illustrates the actual defection rates from physicians' practices over a six-month period relative to patients' overall satisfaction with the care received. On average, 9 percent of patients switched physicians in this relatively brief period and the defection rate was nearly four times higher in the lowest quintile of satisfied patients than in the highest.

Improving service, especially in America's service industries, has

## Figure 7.8: Losing Ground with Every Service Mishap

### A Host of Complaints
*Number of Problems per Visit*

**Physician Office**

| | Physician Office |
|---|---|
| 0 Problems | 27.7% |
| 1–2 Problems | 28.3% |
| 3–6 Problems | 26.9% |
| 7+ Problems | 17.1% |

**Emergency Department**

| | Emergency Department |
|---|---|
| 0 Problems | 20.5% |
| 1–2 Problems | 29.8% |
| 3–6 Problems | 29.2% |
| 7+ Problems | 20.5% |

**Hospital**

| | Hospital |
|---|---|
| 0 Problems | 13.2% |
| 1–2 Problems | 19.8% |
| 3–6 Problems | 26.4% |
| 7+ Problems | 40.6% |

With 7 problems, only 31% of patients rate overall hospital care excellent

Patients Rating Overall Care Excellent

Physician Office

Emergency Department

Hospital

Number of Problems Experienced (per Patient Visit)

### The Good, The Bad, The Ugly

*Problems per Patient Visit*

| | Best Performance | Average | Worst Performance |
|---|---|---|---|
| Emergency Department | 2.13 | 4.15 | 5.83 |
| Physician Office | 1.48 | 3.35 | 6.47 |
| Hospital | 4.19 | 6.61 | 11.23 |

*Source:* Reprinted, with permission, from "Service Excellence: Service Quality Strategies of America's Leading Health Systems"; published by the Health Care Advisory Board, copyright © 1999.

*Differentiation*  185

### Figure 7.9: What if There Were a Better Alternative?

**Opportunity for Breakthrough Service?**

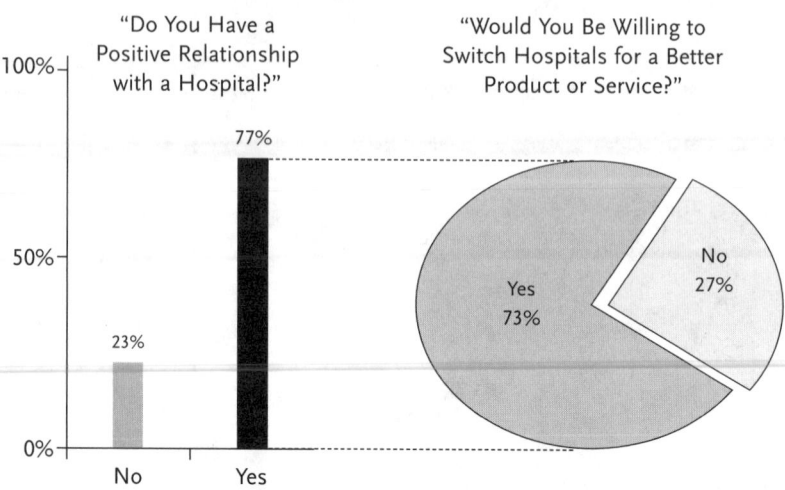

*Source:* Reprinted, with permission, from "Service Excellence: Service Quality Strategies of America's Leading Health Systems"; published by the Health Care Advisory Board, copyright © 1999.

been a major focus of industry leaders for at least the past ten years. This movement has certainly been evident in healthcare as well, with a number of books and national presentations devoted to this topic. Despite all this attention, one would be hard-pressed to point to very many healthcare organizations that have raised their level of service to be consistently excellent (see Figures 7.11 and 7.12).

One final note to reinforce the point that it is service, not technical quality, that seems to matter most to patients at this time. Figures 7.13 and 7.14 delineate the factors that are most important to consumers in recommending a physician or hospital to a family member or friend and the likelihood of making a recommendation related to the overall rating of care provided. Note that few, if any, of the factors influencing the recommendation have to do with the technical quality of the care provided—the care itself or

### Figure 7.10: What if There Were a Better Alternative?

*Defecting for Better Service*

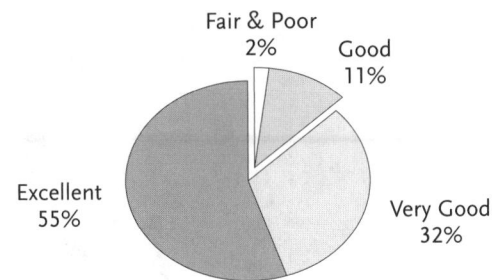

Average Overall Rating of Care

Fair & Poor 2%
Good 11%
Excellent 55%
Very Good 32%

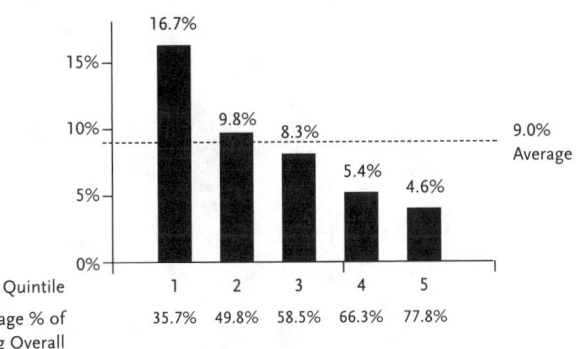

Actual Physician Switching
Six Month Period

16.7%
15%
10%
9.8%  8.3%
5%
5.4%  4.6%
0%

9.0% Average

| Quintile | 1 | 2 | 3 | 4 | 5 |
|---|---|---|---|---|---|
| Average % of Patients Rating Overall Visit Excellent | 35.7% | 49.8% | 58.5% | 66.3% | 77.8% |

the outcome—and virtually all are related to the service experience itself.

The case studies of service leaders in healthcare are drawn from both the not-for-profit and for-profit sectors and are examples of organizations that excel consistently and are differentiated from their competitors through their service strategies.

*Differentiation*   187

**Figure 7.11: Ample Room for Improvement Across the Health System**

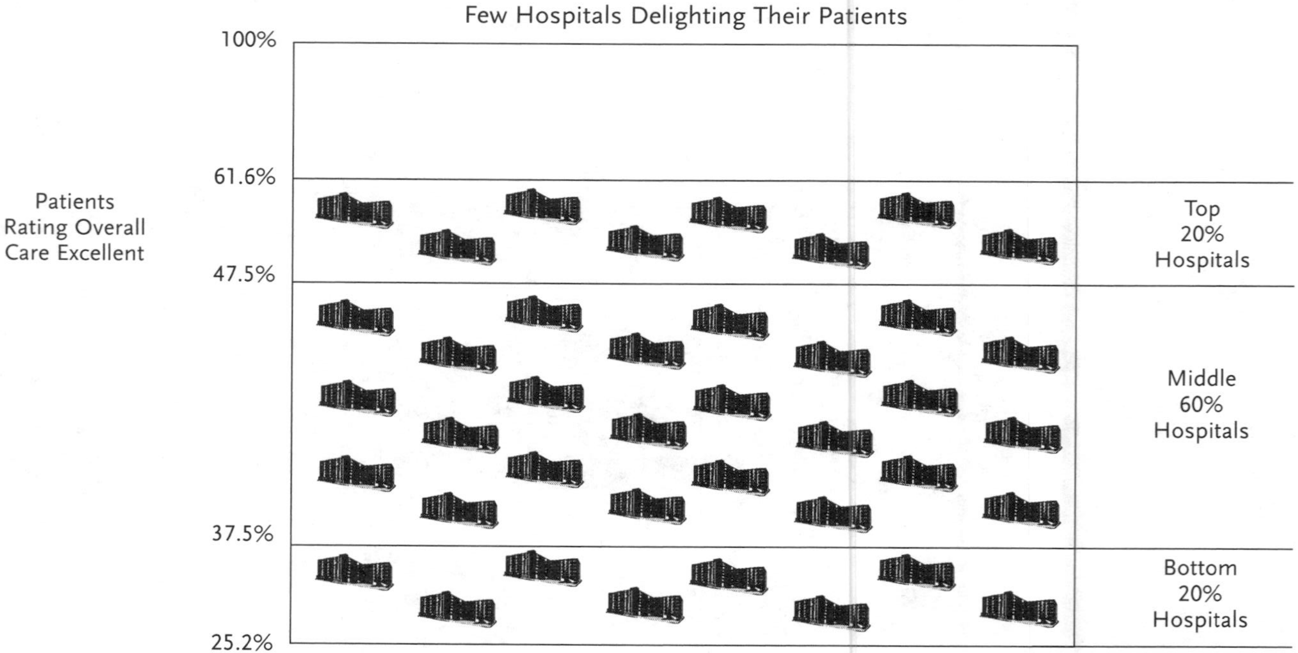

Few Hospitals Delighting Their Patients
Patients Rating Overall Care Excellent
100%
61.6%
47.5%
37.5%
25.2%
Top 20% Hospitals
Middle 60% Hospitals
Bottom 20% Hospitals


*Source:* Reprinted, with permission, from "Service Excellence: Service Quality Strategies of America's Leading Health Systems"; published by the Health Care Advisory Board, copyright © 1999.

**Figure 7.12: Ample Room for Improvement Across the Health System**

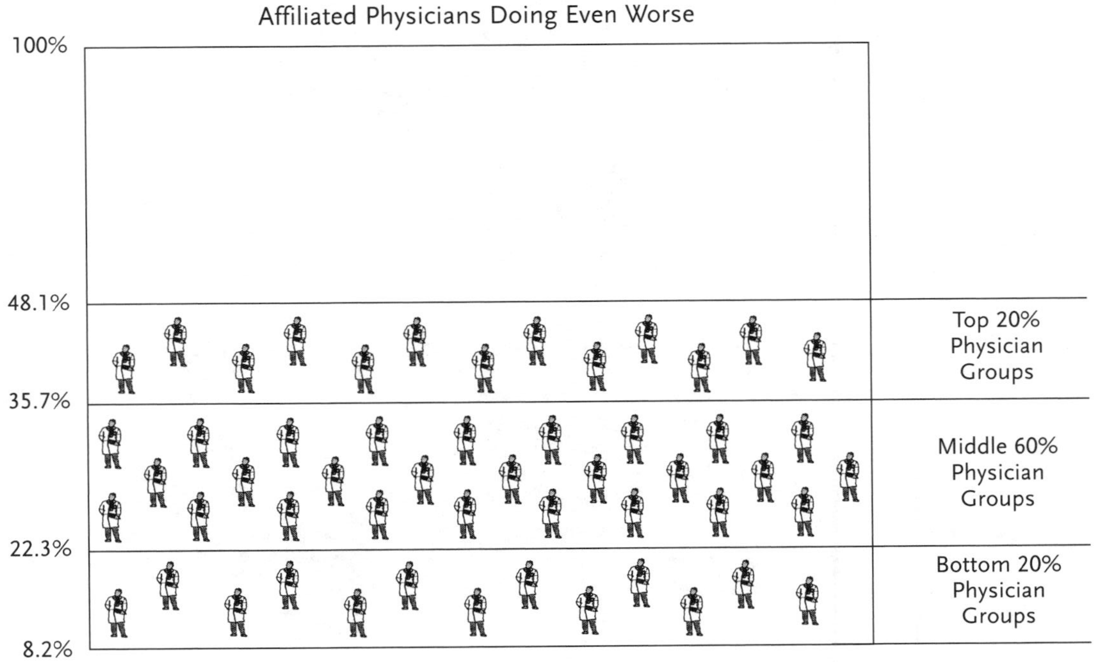

Affiliated Physicians Doing Even Worse

Patients Rating Overall Care Excellent

100%

48.1% — Top 20% Physician Groups

35.7% — Middle 60% Physician Groups

22.3% — Bottom 20% Physician Groups

8.2%

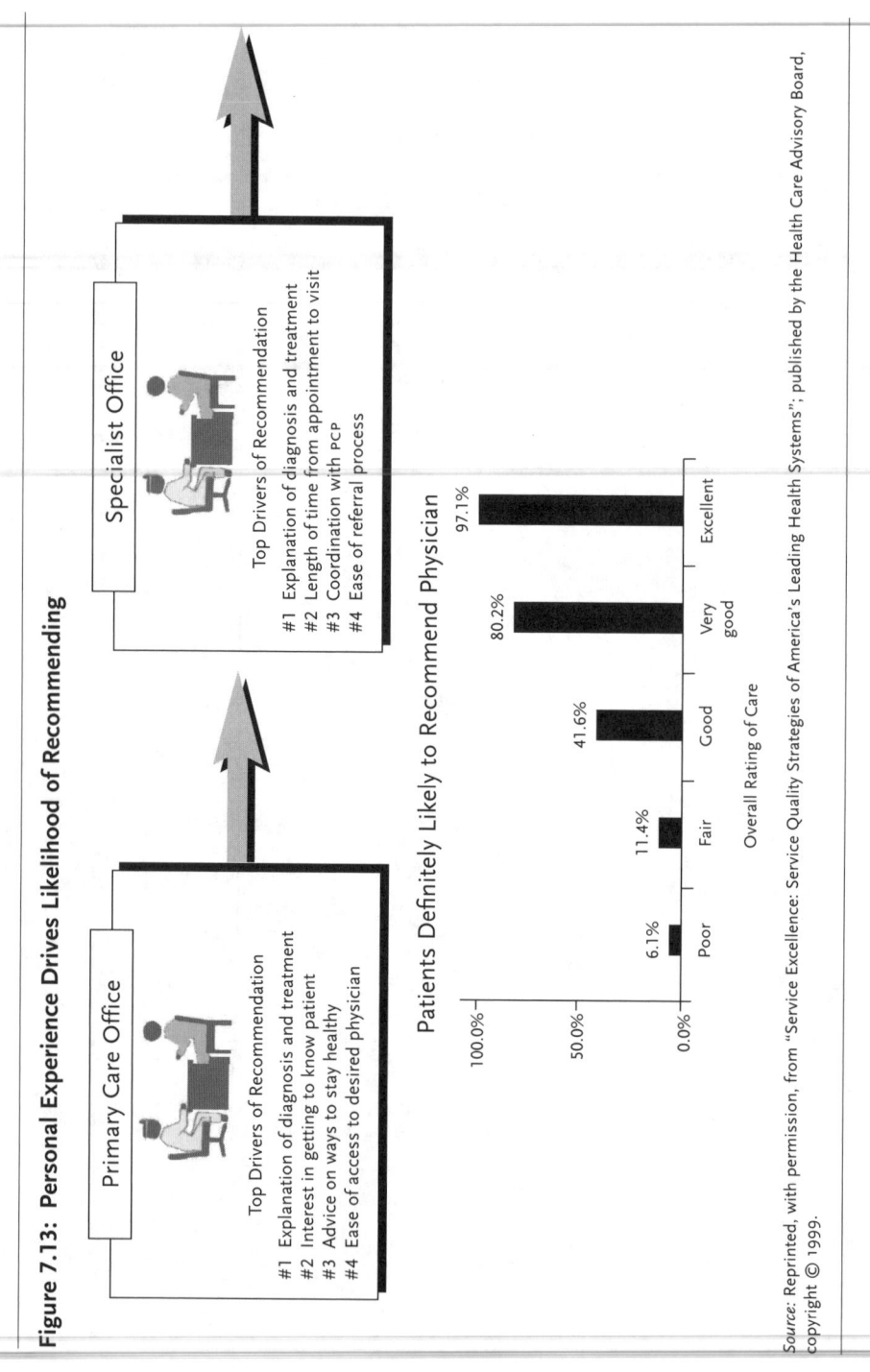

**Figure 7.13: Personal Experience Drives Likelihood of Recommending**

| Primary Care Office | Specialist Office |
|---|---|

**Top Drivers of Recommendation** (Primary Care Office)

#1 Explanation of diagnosis and treatment
#2 Interest in getting to know patient
#3 Advice on ways to stay healthy
#4 Ease of access to desired physician

**Top Drivers of Recommendation** (Specialist Office)

#1 Explanation of diagnosis and treatment
#2 Length of time from appointment to visit
#3 Coordination with PCP
#4 Ease of referral process

**Patients Definitely Likely to Recommend Physician**

| Overall Rating of Care | Percentage |
|---|---|
| Poor | 6.1% |
| Fair | 11.4% |
| Good | 41.6% |
| Very good | 80.2% |
| Excellent | 97.1% |

*Source:* Reprinted, with permission, from "Service Excellence: Service Quality Strategies of America's Leading Health Systems"; published by the Health Care Advisory Board, copyright © 1999.

**Figure 7.14: Personal Experience Drives Likelihood of Recommending**

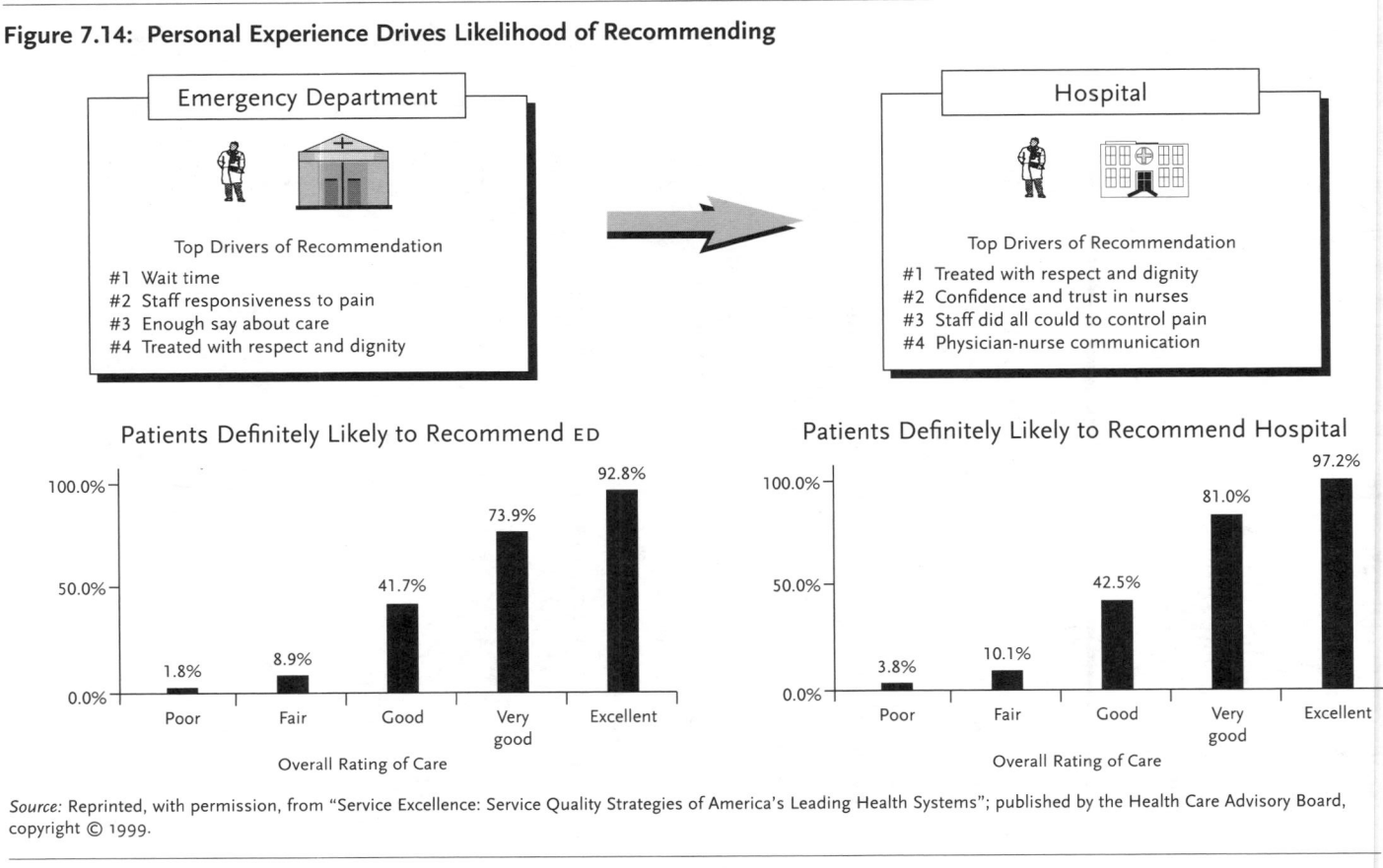

Emergency Department

Top Drivers of Recommendation

#1  Wait time
#2  Staff responsiveness to pain
#3  Enough say about care
#4  Treated with respect and dignity

Hospital

Top Drivers of Recommendation

#1  Treated with respect and dignity
#2  Confidence and trust in nurses
#3  Staff did all could to control pain
#4  Physician-nurse communication

Patients Definitely Likely to Recommend ED

Poor 1.8%
Fair 8.9%
Good 41.7%
Very good 73.9%
Excellent 92.8%

Overall Rating of Care

Patients Definitely Likely to Recommend Hospital

Poor 3.8%
Fair 10.1%
Good 42.5%
Very good 81.0%
Excellent 97.2%

Overall Rating of Care

*Source:* Reprinted, with permission, from "Service Excellence: Service Quality Strategies of America's Leading Health Systems"; published by the Health Care Advisory Board, copyright © 1999.

*Differentiation*   191

## Service Differentiators in Healthcare: Salick Health Care and Griffin Hospital

Salick Health Care has distinguished itself as a service leader in providing outpatient cancer care since its founding in 1985 by Bernard Salick, M.D. Salick Health Care is a pioneer in developing and providing a fully integrated and comprehensive approach to cancer care services. Its model of patient-centered care was developed to provide patients easy access to outpatient oncology and ancillary services in a single facility that maximizes patient comfort and convenience. With access to a full range of diagnostic and treatment services available 24 hours a day and seven days a week, inpatient admissions are often avoided and disruptions to patients' daily routines are minimized. Emergency room visits are also reduced because the Salick centers are always open to handle urgent needs (Salick Health Care 2001).

Salick has also excelled at meeting the psychosocial needs of cancer patients and their families. Individual and group counseling is available and patients have on-site access to multimedia resource centers and research services to enable more active participation in understanding and managing their disease (Salick Health Care 2001).

Salick operates nine full-service cancer centers in California, New York, and Florida in partnership with leading hospitals, systems, and a network of more than 100 physicians. The company also builds specialty clinical programs such as breast centers, stereotactic radiosurgery, and bone-marrow transplantation that allow the center to brand its services and market them to specific target audiences (Salick Health Care 2001).

With an estimated 85 percent of cancer care in the United States delivered in community-based centers or physician offices and more than one million Americans diagnosed with cancer each year (Saphir 1999), Salick appears poised to continue its successful run as a service-differentiated, for-profit healthcare enterprise.

Griffin Hospital is a 160-bed nonprofit, acute care community hospital in Derby, Connecticut, that has also established a holistic, patient-centered approach to healthcare. Representatives from American and foreign hospitals visit Griffin to study the service-oriented care that has led to a remarkable 96 percent patient satisfaction rating (Griffin Health Services Corporation 2001b).

Incorporated into Griffin Hospital's mission and vision is the desire to change the healthcare system from one that is provider dominated to one that is consumer driven, with patients empowered to fully participate in their own healing process.

Notable developments that have engendered Griffin's strong reputation for service excellence include its childbirth center, which opened in 1987 and set a new standard for providing patient choice, convenience, and comfort in terms of the facilities, medical options, and services available to patients. Griffin also developed a Patient Room Service Program that was staffed by hospital volunteers and modeled after hotel amenities to provide more personalized services for patients and their families. Griffin's room service program has been adopted by numerous other healthcare providers (Griffin Health Services Corporation 2001b).

Griffin Hospital adheres to the Planetree approach to patient care, which is a national program dedicated to humanizing healthcare. Griffin is the only Planetree site in the nation to be totally redesigned and newly constructed to accommodate a patient-driven care philosophy. Nurses' workstations are located close to patient bedsides and central work areas have comfortable conference areas for physicians to meet with nurses and patient families. Each unit also has a kitchen where families can prepare meals for patients and dine together (Griffin Health Services Corporation 2001b).

*Fortune* magazine listed Griffin Hospital among the "100 Best Places to Work in America" in 1999 and 2000 (Griffin Health

Services Corporation 2000). *Modern Maturity* magazine, published by the American Association of Retired Persons, named Griffin Hospital to its list of the top 15 "Hospitals with Heart" in 2001 (Griffin Health Services Corporation 2001a). According to Patrick Charmel, president of Griffin Hospital, "Our employees work at the hospital because of personal motivation to serve patients. Our culture and patient-centered-care model empowers employees to develop caring relationships with patients and to provide personalized care in Griffin's healing environment" (Griffin Health Services Corporation 2000).

Griffin's high marks for service excellence have not insulated it from the harsh realities of a difficult operating environment. Griffin's former chief executive officer resigned after two years of losses on the system's HMO and as he faced accusations of spending too much time promoting the hospital as a model for patient-centered care (Morrisey 1998). Griffin's new management team appears confident that they can balance its service differentiation strategy with a strong operational focus to ensure future success.

## PRODUCT DIFFERENTIATION IN HEALTHCARE

The third and final area of differentiation relates to the product itself. Outside of healthcare, those companies that employ a product differentiation strategy generally emphasize the breadth, depth, relatedness, technical features, and excellence of the products they offer. The innovativeness of their products, including continuous refinement of product attributes and development of new products for the market, are also highlighted. Each of these approaches is present to some degree in healthcare, although in general, product differentiation has not been an area of particular or consistently successful emphasis by healthcare providers.

The *breadth, depth,* and *relatedness* aspects of product differentiation have received the most attention recently in healthcare. The development of integrated delivery systems was, at least in part, an attempt by leading healthcare organizations to distinguish themselves based on the scope and extent of services offered. In addition, many systems attempted to increase the relatedness of the services they offered through integration—the provision of well-coordinated care with a high degree of continuity for patients. Although other forces have driven both vertical and horizontal integration of healthcare organizations, particularly efficiencies and market leverage as described in chapters 2 and 3, being able to provide a comprehensive, differentiated product to consumers is certainly one of the main drivers of this recent phenomenon.

*Technical features* and *product excellence* are central to the product differentiation approach used by healthcare organizations and include deploying state-of-the-art equipment, having the most highly qualified staff, and providing centers of excellence. Many healthcare organizations have attempted to remain ahead of their competitors by acquiring state-of-the-art equipment. Historically, university medical centers have acquired the latest equipment to attract and retain highly credentialled and well-qualified staff. By offering capabilities that are unavailable elsewhere, at least locally and in some cases regionally or statewide, university medical centers have been able to consistently distinguish themselves on this dimension from other providers. However, in the past five to ten years, these distinctions have eroded as many community-based organizations increasingly are able to afford the latest technology and staff.

The concept of *centers of excellence* incorporates a number of aspects of product differentiation, but is principally a technical-features competitive strategy. In developing centers of excellence, healthcare organizations build on their strengths in one or more product areas to continually improve their distinctiveness (including of course, quality and service, as well) of selected products. Although sufficient resources are unavailable for all but the largest and most financially strong healthcare organizations to have true centers of excellence in more than a few areas, many healthcare organizations have fallen into the politically expedient trap of trying to make many of their product areas into centers of excellence, with the result that few actually have any areas of true excellence.

*Innovation,* while not wholly separate from the other components of product differentiation, presents another promising approach for healthcare providers. In this category, ongoing innovation is the key to success, including a regular if not continuous stream of product enhancements and new products. In industry, the term "first to market" is used to single out those companies that stand out because of their commitment to product innovation—such companies are nearly always leading others in their industry by announcing the latest generation of new products. While some elements of this strategy are employed by the leading university medical centers, this approach appears to be only a minor aspect of the competitive strategy of these providers.

Although many integrated delivery systems could be cited as examples of the deployment of the product differentiation competitive strategy, it is probably clearer to look at the cases of more focused providers to illustrate the value of this approach. The two cases described below are organizations that are using product differentiation effectively to compete with others in their field.

### Product Differentiators in Healthcare: HealthSouth Corporation and the Texas Heart Institute

Five men pooled their resources and knowledge in 1984 and changed how rehabilitation services would be viewed and structured over the next decade. The culmination of their efforts, establishment of the for-profit HealthSouth Corporation, has led to an integrated services model for rehabilitation that incorporates high-quality diagnostic, surgical, rehabilitation, and occupational health services, which together demonstrate improved outcomes and lower costs (HealthSouth 2001a).

The HealthSouth model is not designed to provide more services, but to offer rehabilitation services within an integrated treatment system. The company's extensive, user-friendly network has garnered the business of large managed care organizations, insurance companies, and employers, while maintaining consistently high patient satisfaction ratings. HealthSouth scored an average of 98 percent in 2000 on Pristine Audits, a yearly, unannounced independent audit that assesses healthcare facilities from the patient's perspective (HealthSouth 2000).

HealthSouth, currently the largest rehabilitation hospital chain in the United States, has more than 2,000 outpatient facilities in its network that provide care for up to 100,000 patients daily, resulting in 10.5 million outpatient visits in 2000 (HealthSouth 2000). Comprehensive inpatient services are available through HealthSouth's 96 rehabilitation hospitals. Most of the HealthSouth facilities have been acquired through an aggressive course of acquisition started in 1993.

Financially the company is demonstrating outstanding performance. In 2000, HealthSouth stock closed up 203 percent and earned the company an enviable top-five performer slot in the S&P 500 (HealthSouth 2000). HealthSouth recognizes the importance of continually investing in its capabilities. In 1999, the company announced plans to invest $1 billion in capital expenditures over the next three to five years for technology updates, facility upgrades, and improvements to management information and collection and billing systems (HealthSouth 2001b). HealthSouth is also continuing to expand its presence as the premier rehabilitation provider through partnerships and alliances, such as those with Delta Airlines and more than 50 professional sports teams. Without losing sight that providing exceptional rehabilitation care is its foundation, HealthSouth is committed to remaining at the forefront of rehabilitation providers by anticipating the needs and trends of the industry and then adapting quickly.

The Texas Heart Institute has dedicated itself to a single mission—reducing the devastating effects of cardiovascular disease, the leading cause of death in the United States, through innovative research, education, and patient programs. Among the institute's most notable achievements are the first successful heart transplant in the United States, the world's first implantation of an artificial heart in a human, and innovative treatments for infants born with congenital heart defects (Texas Heart Institute 2001c).

The nonprofit organization, founded in 1962 by Denton A. Cooley, M.D., is located within St. Luke's Episcopal Hospital in Houston. The institute is organized so that all patient services are provided through St. Luke's and Texas Children's Hospital, which allows the organization to focus on the study and treatment of heart disease, rather than handling the burden of financing a healthcare facility (Texas Heart Institute 2001c).

The Texas Heart Institute is distinguished by impressive volume and success rates. Its physicians (currently numbering 160) have performed more than 100,000 open-heart procedures. About half of the procedures are coronary artery bypass operations with a five-year survival rate of 90 percent and a ten-year survival rate of nearly 75 percent. Since 1972, the institute has performed more than 840 heart transplants, which ranks it as the third largest program in the nation. The institute believes it is differentiated from other heart centers by these large volumes of patients as well as its research that is applied directly to patient care, basic science programs that are examining the causes of heart disease, and a stand-alone postdoctoral program (Texas Heart Institute 2001c).

The institute also sponsors extensive educational programs. Nearly 1,000 physicians attend its symposia each year and the institute's quarterly publication has a distribution of 30,000. In 2001, the Texas Heart Institute was ranked among the nation's top ten heart centers for the 11th consecutive year by the *U.S. News & World Report* (Texas Heart Institute 2001b).

Future success for the institute (currently occupying 65,000 square feet) is anticipated as construction is underway on a new ten-story, 315,000 square-foot building to accommodate the demand for more laboratory space, operating suites, and educational facilities. Slated to open in January 2002, it includes an extensive telemedicine center to share knowledge worldwide and enable physicians to assist patients in rural areas (Texas Heart Institute 2001a).

## CONCLUSION

Differentiation is the competitive strategy with the longest history of application in healthcare. Many provider organizations have tried to distance themselves from competitors on the basis of the quality of the services they offer, but until recently without any data or real proof to back up their claims of quality advantage.

The three forms of differentiation—quality, service, and product—are all being applied to varying degrees by healthcare organizations today. The increasing availability of data and sophisticated approaches will make differentiation an area of prime opportunity for competitive strategy efforts in the foreseeable future and will probably be the next major competitive battlefield following the integration of care in the late 1990s.

## REFERENCES

3M. 2000. "2000 Annual Report." [Online retrieval 9/2/01]. http://www.corporate-ir.net/ireye/ir_site.zhtml?ticker=mmm&script=700.

*Austin Business Journal.* 1998. "Spinoff Gets Good Genes from 3M." [Online article retrieval 9/7/01]. http://austin.bcentral.com/austin/stories/1998/09/28/story6.html.

Chassin, M. R., R. W. Galvin, and the National Roundtable on Health Care Quality. "The Urgent Need to Improve Health Care Quality." *Journal of the American Medical Association* 280 (11): 1000.

Cleverley, W. O., and R. K. Harvey. 1992. "Competitive Strategy for Successful Hospital Management," *Hospital and Health Services Administration* 37 (1): 53–69.

The Coca-Cola Company. 2000. "Annual Report 2000." [Online retrieval 9/4/01]. http://annualreport2000.coca-cola.com/letter/page2.html.

————. 2001. "The World of Coca-Cola." [Online article retrieval 9/4/01]. http://www2.coca-cola.com/about/heritage/worldcocacola.html.

Duncan, W. J. , P. M. Ginter, and L. E. Swayne. 1995. *Strategic Management of Health Care Organizations*, 2nd edition. Boston: Blackwell Business.

East Carolina University School of Business. 2000. Course materials: "Strategy and Competitive Advantage." [Online retrieval 1/7/2000]. www.business.ecu. edu/users/simerlyr/PPT2862.htm.

Fast Company. 1999. "Digital Competition—Laurie A. Tucker." [Online article retrieval 9/17/01]. http://www.fastcompany.com/online/30/tucker.html.

Federal Express Corporation. 2001. "About FedEx." [Online article retrieval 9/7/01]. http://www.fedex.com/us/about/corporation/.

Grant, R. M. 1991. *Contemporary Strategy Analysis: Concepts, Techniques, Applications*. Boston: Blackwell Publishing.

Griffin Health Services Corporation. 2000. "Griffin Hospital Repeats *Fortune*'s 100 Best Places to Work List." [Online article retrieval 9/20/01]. http://www. griffinhealth.org/fortune2001.html.

————. 2001a. "AARP's *Modern Maturity* Names America's 15 Most Friendly Medical Centers." [Online article retrieval 9/20/01]. http://www.griffinhealth. org/news/AARPrelease.html.

————. 2001b. "About Griffin." [Online article retrieval 9/20/01]. http://www. griffinhealth.org/enewspopup.html.

Griffith, J. R. 2000. "Championship Management for Healthcare Organizations." *Journal of Healthcare Management* 45 (1): 19.

Hallam, K. 1999. "Clinton Seeks Action on Medical Errors." *Modern Healthcare*, December 13. [Online article retrieval 8/20/01]. http://www.modernhealthcare. com/archive/members/articles/1999/12/13_2370.php.

HealthSouth. 2000. "HealthSouth 2000 Annual Report." [Online retrieval 9/20/01]. http://www.healthsouth.com/hsus/HSUS/EN_US/annual_report.

————. 2001a. "About HealthSouth." [Online article retrieval 9/20/01]. http://www.healthsouth.com/hsus/HSUS/EN_US/about/articles/aboutIndex.js.

————. 2001b. "Growth Timeline." [Online article retrieval 9/20/01]. http:// www.healthsouth.com/hsus/HSUS/EN_US/about/Articles/growth.jsp?BV.

Hoovers. 2001a. "Minnesota Mining and Manufacturing Company." [Online article retrieval 9/7/01]. http://www.hoovers.com/co/capsule/3/0,2163, 11003,00.html.

————. 2001b. "Sony Corporation." [Online article retrieval 9/10/01]. http:// hoovers.com/co/capsule/5/0,2163,41885,00.html.

————. 2001c. "FedEx Corporation." [Online article retrieval 9/7/01]. http://www.hoovers.com/co/capsule/2/0,2163,10552,00.html.

Langabeer, J. 1998. "Competitive Strategy in Turbulent Healthcare Markets: An Analysis of Financially Effective Teaching Hospitals." *Journal of Healthcare Management* 43 (6): 512–25.

Johns Hopkins University and Johns Hopkins Medicine. 2001. "Fast Facts." [Online retrieval 9/18/01]. http://www.jhu.edu/news_info/fastfacts.html.

Luke, R. D. and J. W. Begun. 1993. "Strategy Making in Health Care Organizations." In *Health Care Management: Organization Design and Behavior,* 3rd edition, edited by S. Shortell and A. Kaluzny. Albany, NY: Delmar, 2000.

MacStravic, S. 2000. "The Ultimate Quality Indicator." *Health Care Strategic Management* February: 12.

Maytag Corporation. 2000. "2000 Annual Report." [Online retrieval 9/6/01]. http://www.maytag.com.

————. 2001. "About Maytag Corporation." [Online article retrieval 9/6/01]. http://www.maytag.com/mths/ou.../about_maytag.jsp?.

Morrisey, J. 1998. "Planetree Model Gets New Caretaker." *Modern Healthcare,* April 20. [Online article retrieval 8/21/01]. http://modernhealthcare.com/archive/members/articles/1998/04/20_14390.php.

Moore, S. T. and K. D. Bopp. 1999. "How Consumers Evaluate Health Care Quality: Part I." *Health Care Marketing Quarterly* 16 (4): 4.

Nordstrom. 2001a. [Online article retrieval 9/13/01]. http://about.nordstrom.com/aboutus/.

————. 2001b. "2001 Annual Report." [Online retrieval 9/13/01]. www.nordstrom.com.

Pointer, D. D. 1990. "Offering-Level Strategy Formulation in Health Service Organizations." *Health Management Review* 15 (3): 11–19.

Porter, M. 1985. *Competitive Advantage: Creating and Sustaining Superior Performance.* New York: Simon and Schuster Trade.

PR Newswire. 2000. "Maytag to Acquire Amana." [Online article retrieval 9/6/01]. http://www.prnewswire.com/cgi-bin/micro_stories.pl?.

Robinson, S. and M. Brodie. 1997. "Understanding the Quality Challenge for Health Consumers: The Kaiser/AHCPR Survey." *Journal of Quality Improvement* 23 (5): 239.

Salick Health Care. 2001. "Salick Health Care." [Online article retrieval 9/14/01]. http://www.salick.com/company/index.html.

Saphir, A. 1999. "At the Center of Cancer Care: For-Profit Outpatient Centers Are Playing Bigger Role in Treatment, Clinical Trials." *Modern Healthcare,* May 15. [Online article retrieval 8/21/01]. http://www.modernhealthcare.com/archive/members/articles/1999/05//31_3548.php.

Shortell, S. M., E. M. Morrison, and B. Friedman. 1990. *Strategic Choices for America's Hospitals: Managing Change in Turbulent Times.* San Francisco: Jossey-Bass.

Sony Corporation. 2001a. "History." [Online article retrieval 9/10/01]. http://www.sony.co.jp/en/sonyinfo/corporateinfo/history/prospectus.html/.

Texas Heart Institute. 2001a. "Message from Our President." [Online article retrieval 9/20/01]. http://www.tmc.edu/thi/about.html.

———. 2001b. "Texas Heart Institute at St. Luke's Episcopal Hospital Again Ranked Among Nation's Top 10 Heart Centers." [Online article retrieval 9/20/01]. http://www.tmc.edu/thi/usn2001.html.

———. 2001c. "Summary of Programs." [Online article retrieval 9/20/01]. http://www.tmc.edu/thi/summary.html.

University of Minnesota. 2001. "3M Develops a Way to Find Future Innovators." [Online article retrieval 9/7/01]. http://mustang.coled.umn.edu/inventing/Innovation.html.

University of Pennsylvania Health System. 2001a. "What Is UPHS?" [Online article retrieval 9/15/01]. http://www.uphs.upenn.edu/about_uphs/what_ is.html.

———. 2001b. "Commitment to Excellence." [Online article retrieval 9/15/01]. http://www.uphs.upenn.edu/about_uphs/commit.html.

Worldcare.com. 2001. "Johns Hopkins Medicine: Creating New Knowledge for Health." [Online article retrieval 9/19/01]. http://www.worldcare.com/e_consultations/consortium/johns_hopkins.html.

Yahoo!Finance. 2001a. "Profile—Coca-Cola Company." [Online article retrieval 9/5/01]. http://biz.yahoo.com/p/k/ko.html.

———. 2001b. "Market Likes 3M's Plan." [Online article retrieval 9/7/01]. http://biz yahoo.com/mf/010702/news03_010702.html.

202    *Improve Your Competitive Strategy*

# CHAPTER 8

# Raising Competitive Strategy to a Higher Level: Applying Sophisticated Approaches and Analytical Techniques

## INTRODUCTION

THE PRECEDING CHAPTERS have provided a thorough review of state-of-the-art-healthcare competitive strategy. As the market for healthcare services has become more competitive, providers have responded with increasingly pronounced and more complex strategic moves. Yet, in comparison to the overwhelming majority of American companies, healthcare organizations employ more basic approaches and analytical techniques in competitive strategy.

As discussed in the previous chapters, for-profit healthcare organizations use somewhat more advanced approaches and techniques than their not-for-profit counterparts. But neither not-for-profits nor for-profits avail themselves of the full array of approaches and techniques that exist today and are employed to varying degrees in both American and international for-profit companies. The material that follows synthesizes the ideas and tools that are available and should begin to be applied by healthcare organizations to increase their competitive armamentarium and raise their competitive strategies to a much higher level.

This chapter will focus on three interrelated aspects of competitive analysis, beginning with the broadest level, *industry analysis,* and proceeding to *competitor analysis* and *competitor intelligence*. These aspects of competitive analysis will illustrate the need for healthcare organizations to devote more energy and attention to their external environments and to collection and analysis of external information that will improve their ability to react to, anticipate, and then influence and mold their competitors and markets.

## INDUSTRY ANALYSIS

In one of Porter's earliest works he wrote "[t]he essence of strategy formulation is coping with competition" and "[t]he state of competition in an industry depends on five basic forces" (Porter 1998) (see Figure 8.1). His framework for industry analysis has been adopted by most experts in the field with minor modifications and variations.

The five basic forces that determine the degree of competition in an industry are:

1. Threat of new entrants
2. Threat of substitute products and services
3. Bargaining power of buyers
4. Bargaining power of suppliers
5. Rivalry among existing firms

The stronger the forces collectively, the worse the prospects are for long-term superior performance, while the opposite is true when the forces are, in sum, weak. "Whatever their collective strength, the corporate strategist's goal is to find a position in the industry where his or her company can best defend itself against these forces or can influence them in its favor" (Porter 1998). When reviewing this framework from the perspective of the healthcare organization, it may be useful to think about the "industry" in less global terms, since few, if any, providers compete in all segments of all markets. Thus, the relevant industry may be a product market

**Figure 8.1: Porter's "Five Forces of Competition" Framework**

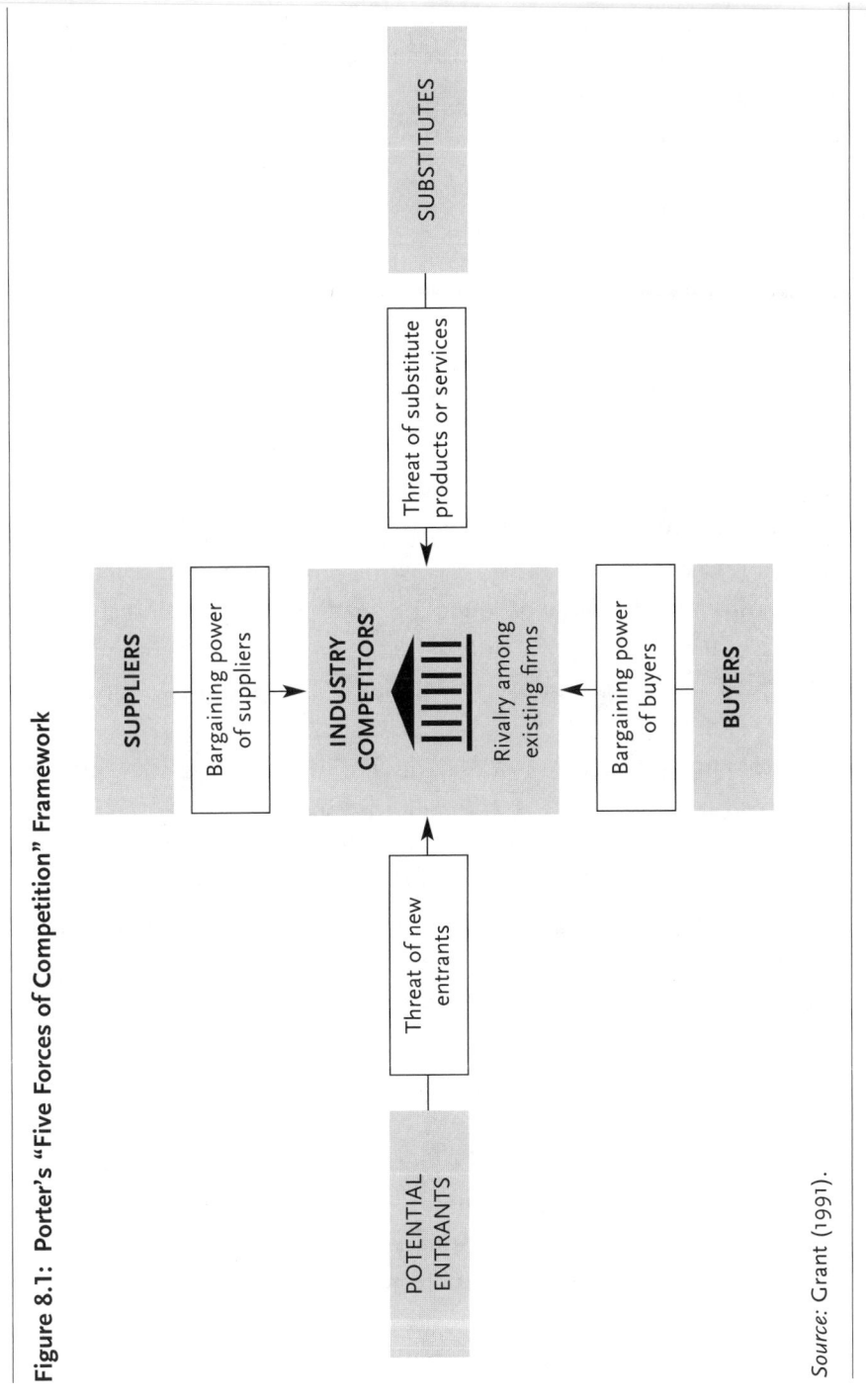

*Source:* Grant (1991).

or a geographic market for a family of products. The issue of the definition of industry boundaries is a thorny one and is addressed in some detail later in this chapter.

A brief description of the nature and effect of the five competitive forces follows (see also Figure 8.2).

### New Entrants

"New entrants to an industry bring new capacity, the desire to gain market share, and often substantial resources" (Porter 1998). Outside of healthcare, new entrants are usually attracted by the profitability of the industry or some segment of it. Recently, the attraction of new entrants due to profitability has been increasingly prevalent in healthcare, too, with the growing presence of for-profit firms in many product and market segments and some similar not-for-profit behavior as well. New entrants may find it difficult to enter the industry because of sizable capital requirements to start up and become operational, cost or scale advantages of incumbents, brand recognition and existing customer loyalty of established firms, control of product distribution channels by existing firms, government and legal barriers, and the threat of retaliation by established firms. These barriers to entry may pose major, moderate, or minor problems to potential new industry entrants.

### Substitutes

The availability and sustainability of substitute products or services have an obvious impact on competitiveness. If few available or suitable substitutes are present in the market, as in the case with hospital critical care services, prices are usually high and demand is "inelastic" or does not vary much overall based on price. If many available or suitable substitutes are present, as is the case for some

**Figure 8.2: The Structural Determinants of Competitive Pressure**

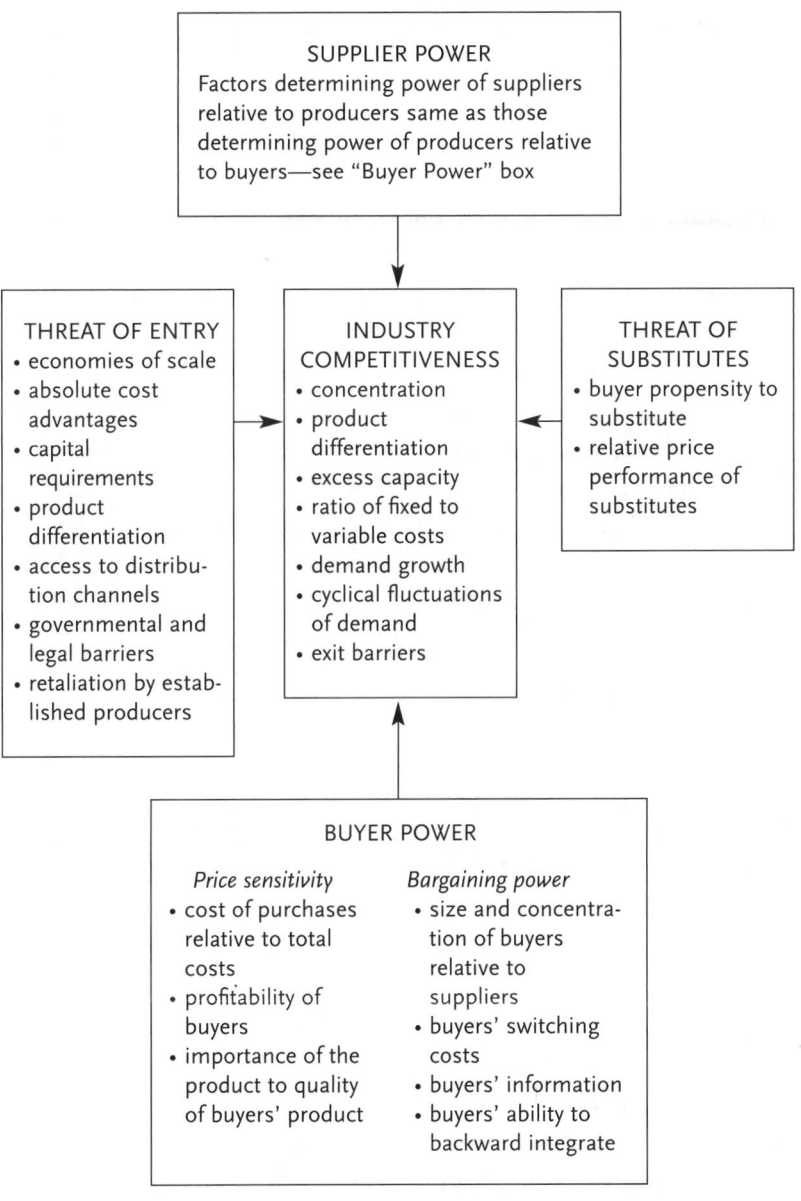

ambulatory care services, prices are constrained and demand may change considerably depending on price. Competitiveness is also affected by how close the substitutes are for the products or services in question and how well these substitutes perform in relation to their prices.

## Bargaining Power of Buyers and Suppliers

As it relates to both of these topics, Grant (1991) notes:

> The firms in an industry operate in two types of market: The markets for *inputs* and the market for *outputs*. In the markets for inputs they purchase raw materials, components, finance, and labor services from the suppliers of these factors of production; in the markets for outputs they sell their products and services to customers, who may be distributors, consumers, or other manufacturers. In both these markets the relative profitability of the two parties to a transaction depends upon relative economic power.

Porter (1991) comments:

> Suppliers can exert bargaining power on participants in an industry by raising prices or reducing the quality of purchased goods and services. Powerful suppliers can thereby squeeze profitability out of an industry unable to recover cost increases in its own prices. . . Customers likewise can force down prices, demand higher quality or more service, and play competitors off against each other—all at the expense of industry profits.

Both buyers and suppliers have greater bargaining power if they are price sensitive and if they are large and well-informed. Until fairly recently, these conditions did not characterize the buyers in the market facing healthcare providers, and one can argue that increased price sensitivity among larger and smarter buyers is the single most significant factor affecting the competitiveness of the healthcare market in the past ten years. Suppliers in healthcare delivery are, on the other hand, many, diverse, and fairly profitable and do not exert a great deal of influence on healthcare competition.

## Rivalry

In many industries, competition among firms within the industry is the most important factor affecting overall competitiveness. In those industries where firms compete aggressively, prices may fall below costs and significant, across-the-board losses may result. Except in rare instances in healthcare, competition has been relatively insignificant and benign until fairly recently.

The degree of rivalry in an industry is affected by the following:

- *Concentration*—the number of competitors and their relative sizes; more, smaller competitors lead to more competition.
- *Diversity*—the more similar firms are in terms of their history, culture, operations, and strategies, the less competition there usually is.
- *Differentiation*—the more differences in competitors' products or services, the more competition generally occurs.
- *Excess capacity*—encourages greater competition.
- *Exit barriers*—also lead to greater competition.
- *Cost conditions*—the greater the potential to reap scale economies, the more competition is likely.

Certainly, many of these factors characterize healthcare markets and, with the lessening influence of a number of regulatory factors, have spurred creation of a much more competitive industry in recent years.

Achieving a better understanding of industry (or local and regional product and market segments) conditions and competitiveness is the first step toward formulating competitive strategies that will be effective. Only then can the organization begin to position itself both offensively and defensively as well as prepare for changes in competitive conditions based on shifts in underlying forces in the industry. The next step to improving competitive fitness is gaining a much more comprehensive and in-depth understanding of the competitors facing the organization and the specific product and market components of it. In this regard, Grant (1991) adds that "[o]bservations show that, in most markets, the outcome of the competitive process is determined not just by industry structure but also by the sequence, timing, and mutual perceptions of each firm's competitive moves."

## COMPETITOR ANALYSIS

Before proceeding to describe competitor analysis in detail, two important, related issues deserve comment: where to draw industry boundaries and the value of segmentation.

While the challenges of defining industry boundaries (i.e., what is to be included within the industry being analyzed and the relevant competitors within the industry) within healthcare are great and seem unique, Grant (1991) indicates "[n]o industry has clear boundaries either in terms of products or geographical areas." He suggests that the major criterion to be applied in determining industry boundaries is substitutability: do customers consider the products (or services) of each firm to be close substitutes for one another and can each firm produce roughly similar products or services as other potential competitors? Faulkner and Bowman (1995) suggest that industries consist of "groups of companies who are aware of each other as competitors in a particular market, and who are collectively separated from other such groups by mobility barriers" (the latter being these barriers that help to keep the groups separate such as geography, government regulations and licenses, proprietary technology, etc.).

Faulkner and Bowman's commentary suggests that healthcare should not be considered one industry for the purposes of competitive analysis and must be segmented into appropriate components. Most industries can be segmented in a number of different ways, with the most obvious being based on different types of products, customers, price ranges, or geographical areas served.

Under this construct, healthcare delivery can be viewed as composed of thousands of different industry segments. Such segments should be constructed for competitive analysis purposes with recognition of the dangers of drawing the boundaries too broadly, namely deriving competitive inferences based on the characteristics and behaviors of those firms that are largely noncompetitors and of drawing the boundaries too narrowly and ignoring the influences of actual or emerging competitors.

A basic framework for competitor analysis is presented in Figure 8.3. At the outset, Grant (1991) notes that "[c]ompetitor analysis has three main purposes:

1. "To forecast competitors' future strategies and decisions
2. To predict competitors' likely reactions to a firm's strategy and competitive initiatives
3. To determine how competitors' behavior can be influenced to the benefit of the initiating firm

"For all three purposes, the key requirement is to understand competitors in order to predict their choices of strategy and tactics and likely reactions to environmental changes and any competitive moves initiated by one's own company."

Each of the main components of competitor analysis, consistent with Figure 8.3, is described below.

### Identifying Competitors' Goals

Competitors may have a variety of goals, among them financial, market, technological, and social. They may have goals at different levels in the company, such as corporate, site, and business unit.

**Figure 8.3: A Framework for Competitor Analysis**

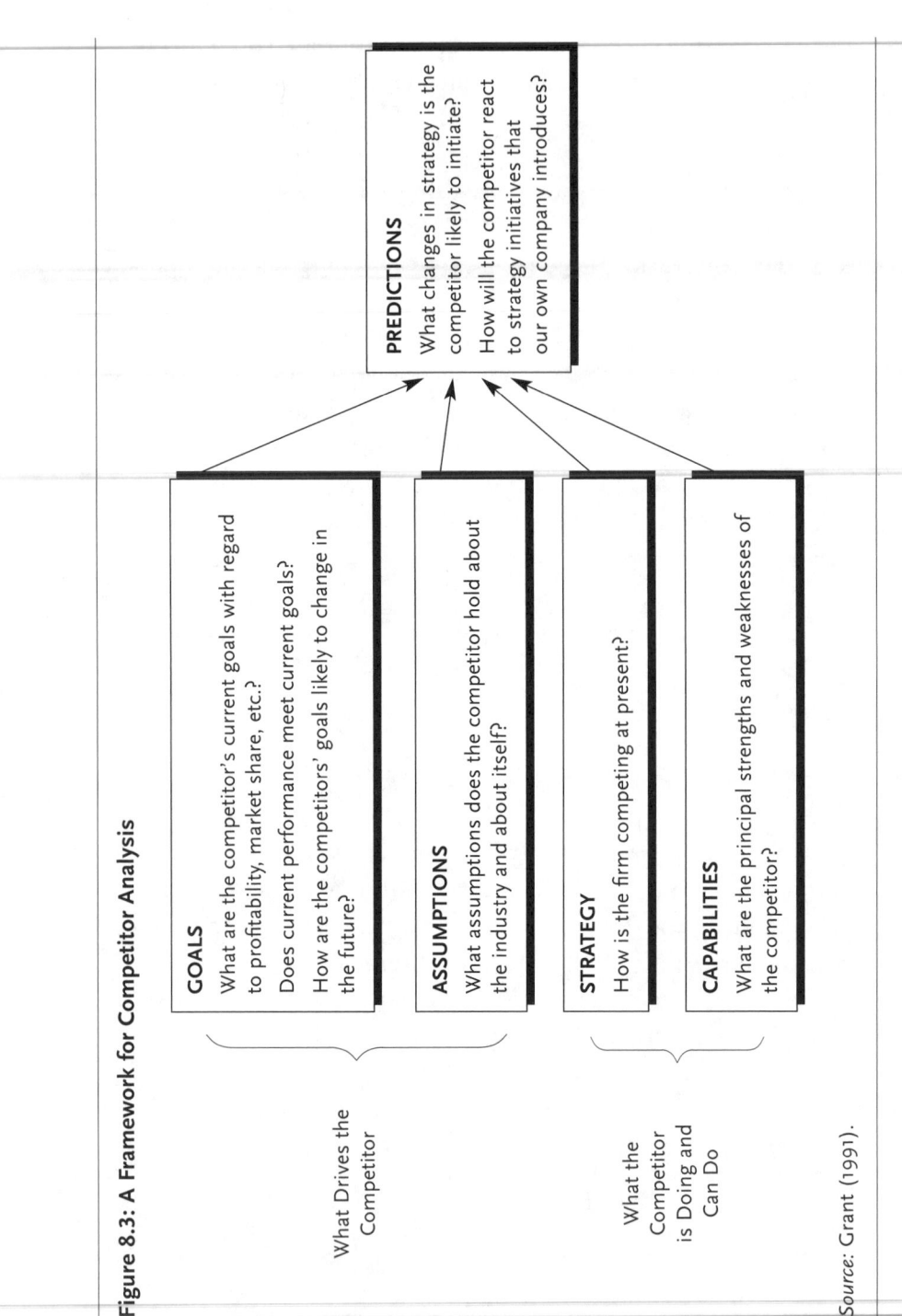

**GOALS**

What are the competitor's current goals with regard to profitability, market share, etc.?

Does current performance meet current goals?

How are the competitors' goals likely to change in the future?

**ASSUMPTIONS**

What assumptions does the competitor hold about the industry and about itself?

**STRATEGY**

How is the firm competing at present?

**CAPABILITIES**

What are the principal strengths and weaknesses of the competitor?

What Drives the Competitor

What the Competitor is Doing and Can Do

**PREDICTIONS**

What changes in strategy is the competitor likely to initiate?

How will the competitor react to strategy initiatives that our own company introduces?

*Source:* Grant (1991).

Identifying these goals helps to reveal how satisfied each competitor is with its current position and how likely each is to change strategy, react to external events, or react to competitor moves. This analysis also could assist in determining if positions exist in the industry that are not very threatening to competitors and if head-on competition can be avoided.

### Identifying Competitors' Assumptions About the Industry

Competitors' assumptions about the industry and other competitors include beliefs about future demands and industry trends and their effects. Such assumptions often encompass belief in conventional wisdom or historic rules of thumb that are at odds with market conditions, thus leading to blind spots in competitive strategy. Grant (1991) points out that major American automobile manufacturers' belief in the 1960s that small cars were unprofitable set the stage for the Japanese and European invasion of the American market. Competitors' assumptions about themselves, including strengths and weaknesses, historical or emotional ties to products or policies, organizational values, and the behavior of competitors over time can also be very revealing.

### Identifying Competitors' Current Strategy

Grant (1991) suggests that "[I]n the absence of any forces for change, a reasonable assumption is that the company will continue to compete in the future in much the same way as it competes at the present." Current strategies may be explicit and appear in annual reports, public statements, etc., or implicit and be inferred primarily by observing or analyzing what the company does. Identifying how strategies have changed over time is important and revealing of the likelihood and direction of future changes. Such changes should be tracked, with causal factors determined, as well as analyzing the implications of the aspects of each competitor's situation and performance that could lead to a change in strategy.

## Identifying Competitors' Capabilities

The question here is, do the competitors' capabilities present a serious competitive threat? Subsidiary questions include: What are the competitors best at doing and worst at doing? How consistently do they follow their strategy? Is each growing stronger or weaker and in what areas? Key resources such as financial reserves, capital equipment, workforces, brand loyalty, and management skills and capabilities, including research and development, production, distribution, and marketing, are indicative of the ability of competitors to react to external changes or competitor moves. Also of importance is whether the competitors have quick response capabilities, ability to adapt to change, and staying power.

To complete the competitor analysis, the implications for the organization's or business unit's competitive strategy should be determined through the answers to four key questions:

1. What are the effects of the interaction of probable competitor moves that have been identified?
2. Are organizations' strategies converging and likely to clash?
3. Do organizations have sustainable growth rates that match the industry's forecasted growth rate, or will a gap be created that will invite entry?
4. What is the net effect of probable moves in terms of implications for industry or market structure?

In summary, Grant (1991) concludes:

Even the industry segment is too high a level of aggregation for most firms. To gain an intimate understanding of competition, to predict competitive threats, and to influence competitors' behavior, analysis must extend down to the level of individual competitors. In industries where a company faces a few close competitors, it is not possible to understand competition without understanding the competitors themselves . . . "Getting inside" competitors in order to understand and influence competitive interaction lies at the heart of strategy analysis. An essential characteristic of successful strategists, whether corporate chief executives, military commanders, political leaders, or chess players, is their ability to insightfully analyze their opponents.

## COMPETITOR INTELLIGENCE

To effectively perform the competitor analysis described above requires a substantial amount of data. The amount and comprehensiveness of the data required go beyond what is typically available in a healthcare organization. A new and different approach is called for to meet the challenges presented by this task.

Only through a systematic approach to the collection, compilation, cataloging, analysis, and subsequent communication of information (versus data) to management (see Figure 8.4) can the scope and extent of competitor strategy analysis described above be carried out successfully. While there can be significant variation in the degree of completeness of data included in a formal competitor intelligence tracking system, some systematization is required to ensure that it occurs on an ongoing basis and is carried out reasonably efficiently. In regard to the "how" of such a process, Porter (1998) writes:

> One observes a variety of alternative ways firms organize to perform these functions in practice. They range from a competitor analysis group that is part of the planning department and performs all the functions (perhaps drawing on others in the organization for collecting field data); to a competitor intelligence coordinator who performs the compiling, cataloging, and communication functions; to a system in which the strategist does it

## Figure 8.4: Functions of a Competitor Intelligence System

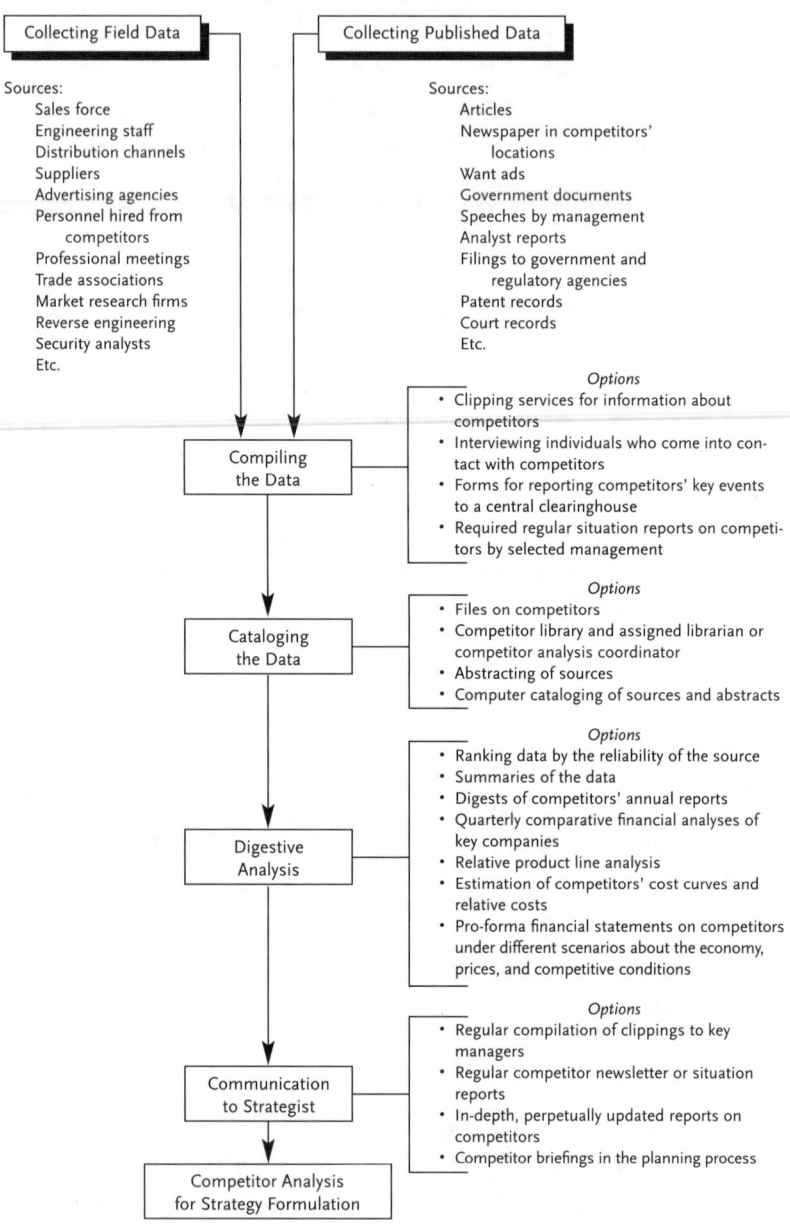

all informally. All too often, however, no one is made responsible for the competitor analysis at all. There seems to be no single correct way to collect competitor data, but it is clear that someone must take an active interest or much useful information will be lost. Top management can do a lot to stimulate the effort by requiring sophisticated profiles of competitors as part of the planning process. At a minimum, some manager with the responsibility to serve as the focal point for competitor intelligence gathering seems to be necessary.

Whatever the mechanism chosen for competitor intelligence gathering, there are benefits to be gained from one that is formal and involves some documentation. It is all too easy for bits and pieces of data to be lost, and the benefits that come only from combining these bits and pieces thereby foregone. Analyzing competitors is too important to handle haphazardly.

The increasing importance of accurate and complete competitor intelligence is underscored by the appearance of increasing amounts of literature on the subject. For example, Pollard (1999) devoted an entire text to it. He indicates:

[a] number of trends have combined in recent years to increase the need for *systematic* systems of competitor intelligence:

- Increasing competition
- Increased size of markets (globalisation of markets)
- Increased pace of change (e.g., by governments deregulating)
- Increasing size of companies (e.g., from globalisation and acquisitions)
- Greater access to information (e.g., the Internet, intranets and extranets)
- Development of sophisticated search engines (e.g., Alta Vista)
- Improvements in technology making decentralised systems possible
- Greater knowledge of the benefits of competitor intelligence.

Pollard (1999) also notes:

> From the collection point of view, the advent of the web browser interface and the growth of useful websites on the Internet is revolutionising the collection of external competitor intelligence. And with the growth of intranets, competitor intelligence managers will have at their terminals a 'one stop shopping' gateway to an enormous world of electronic information.
>
> In the next five years competitor intelligence will further integrate itself into business strategic and tactical thought and practice. Decision making in the real world is frequently made in ignorance and with fragmentary information about business conditions, including those relating to competitors. Business strategy and intelligence strategy need to be run side by side if companies are to make at least neo-rational decisions. In the future, success in business will increasingly go to senior managers who know how to use competitor intelligence.

## CONCLUSION

A wealth of general business literature describes how to apply sophisticated approaches and analytical techniques to competitive strategy. A few of these resources are cited in this chapter. Healthcare providers are no longer operating in benign competitive sectors and cannot afford to continue to use basic analytical frameworks and techniques. Nor can they continue to pretend that only friendly competition exists among competitors as an excuse for failure to apply modern approaches and techniques. Organizations that fail to raise their competitive analysis approaches and techniques to a much higher level will fall further and further behind. The tools are now there and providers must use them more regularly and systematically.

# REFERENCES

Faulkner, D., and C. Bowman. 1995. *The Essence of Competitive Strategy*, p. 2. Upper Saddle River, NJ: Prentice Hall.

Grant, R. M. 1991. *Contemporary Strategy Analysis: Concepts, Techniques, Applications*. Boston: Blackwell Publishing.

Pollard, A. 1999. *Competitor Intelligence: Strategy, Tools and Techniques of Competitive Advantage*. London: Financial Times Publishing.

Porter, M. E. 1998. *On Competition*. Boston: Harvard Business School Publishing.

———. 1980. *Competitive Strategy: Techniques for Analyzing Industries and Competitors*. New York: The Free Press, a division of Macmillan, Inc.

# The Future of Healthcare Competitive Strategy

## INTRODUCTION

ONE OF THE main themes of the most recent research on competitive strategy is that it is not sufficient merely to gain competitive advantage, but that advantage must be sustained over time. Whereas chapter 8 presents the case for a move from basic to advanced competitive approaches and techniques in a traditional sense, chapter 9 suggests that even some of these advancements may not be enough to stay competitive. Taken together, these chapters suggest that healthcare organizations must get on a fast track now and improve their competitive strategy approaches and techniques to stay viable into the twenty-first century.

In one of the earliest discussions of this subject in the healthcare literature, Shortell, Morrison, and Friedman (1990) suggest that the key to sustaining competitive advantage "is the ability to add greater value for the customer than competitors." They present six general strategies for hospitals to sustain competitive advantage:

1. *Selective diversification*—focused, related diversification that complements and plays off the organization's strengths and capabilities

2. *Careful deployment of slack resources*—having and making available funds, personnel, and other resources to promote growth and development

3. *Continuous market research and learning*—rapid market change requires ongoing research of customers, their characteristics, and how best to reach each segment

4. *Flexible strategic planning and control*—balancing centralized versus decentralized approaches and structure and formality versus fluidity are the key components that need to be varied based on the organization and its situation

5. *Work effectively with physicians*—success in strategy implementation depends on the cooperation and often the active involvement of physicians

6. *Operate within the organization's comfort zone*—organizations operating outside their strategic comfort zone are believed to perform more poorly than those operating within it

## SUSTAINING COMPETITIVE ADVANTAGE: THE BUSINESS PERSPECTIVE

Within the general business literature, there are two somewhat different schools of thought about how to obtain and then maintain competitive advantage. Burns (2000) describes the differences between these perspectives:

> While the Porter five forces analysis suggests where the firm should compete, the resource-based view of the firm suggests how it should compete. That is, Porter's model indicates what industries or market segments might be attractive to enter by virtue of offering defensible cost positions, differentiation positions, or niche positions. But the source of these defensible positions (the source of Porter's generic strategies) is the set of resources and capabilities possessed by the firm. Strategy is thus concerned with matching the firm's resources and capabilities to

the opportunities presented by the external environment (industry, market). . .

Strategy is thus bounded by the structure of competition within the firm's industry and markets, which suggests some positions to occupy. But, within these bounds, strategy and strategic decision making consist of a "war of movement" between firms engaged in developing resources and capabilities that confer competitive advantage. The building blocks of competitive strategy, then, are not the firm's products or services but rather the firm's business processes and infrastructure. For Porter, these processes and infrastructure enable the firm to pursue one of three generic strategies—i.e., be the low-cost producer, develop differentiated (new) products and services, or identify and serve niche markets. For others (Day and Reibstein 1997), these processes and infrastructure enable firms to develop three "value disciplines" (similar to strategies) that maximize different types of customer value: operational excellence (e.g., low price and dependability), customer responsiveness (e.g., customized product, personalized service), and performance superiority (high technical performance, innovation).

Finally, it is important to view the firm's resources and capabilities in dynamic rather than static terms. . . . Given this fact of life, the firm can either try to erect barriers to imitation that impede competitors from appropriating its competitive advantage, or the firm can decide to continually invest in developing new resources and capabilities.

## THE DYNAMIC NATURE OF COMPETITIVE STRATEGY

Day and Reibstein (1997) develop further the concept of the dynamic nature of competitive strategy in their work. Numerous examples are presented of companies that failed to adapt to a changing market structure, their competitors' moves, or both. Two brief cases cited by Day and Reibstein clearly illustrate these situations:

- In the 1970s, Okidata made an excellent dot-matrix printer and captured a large share of the market, but failed to adapt and lost its leadership position and most of its market when Hewlett-Packard introduced first an ink-jet printer and then laser models.
- A bank opened on Saturdays in addition to its normal weekdays to gain an advantage over competitors; while early on the move was successful in attracting new customers, shortly the bank's rivals also opened on Saturdays, thus offsetting the first bank's advantage. The net effect of this move was to increase the cost of doing business, since the same amount of banking was now spread over six days rather than five.

Day and Reibstein (1997) argue for a four-phase approach to address the dynamic nature of competitive strategy (see Figure 9.1) consisting of the following elements:

1. *Understand advantages in a changing environment.* Determine what advantages the organization has over competitors, what the underlying factors are that create these advantages, how the advantages change over time, and what externalities will affect advantage in the future, especially public policy and technology.
2. *Anticipate competitors' actions.* Identify and dissect the competitive games of rivals, gain an understanding of competitors' motives and interpretation of rivals' actions, and forecast how these will change over time due to competitive interactions.
3. *Formulate dynamic strategies.* Explore the firm's strategic options and constraints on those options, analyze alternatives for responding to or preempting competitors' moves, and determine what constraints exist on competitive strategies, especially irreversible moves, investments, and antitrust.

**Figure 9.1: Formulating Dynamic Competitive Strategies**

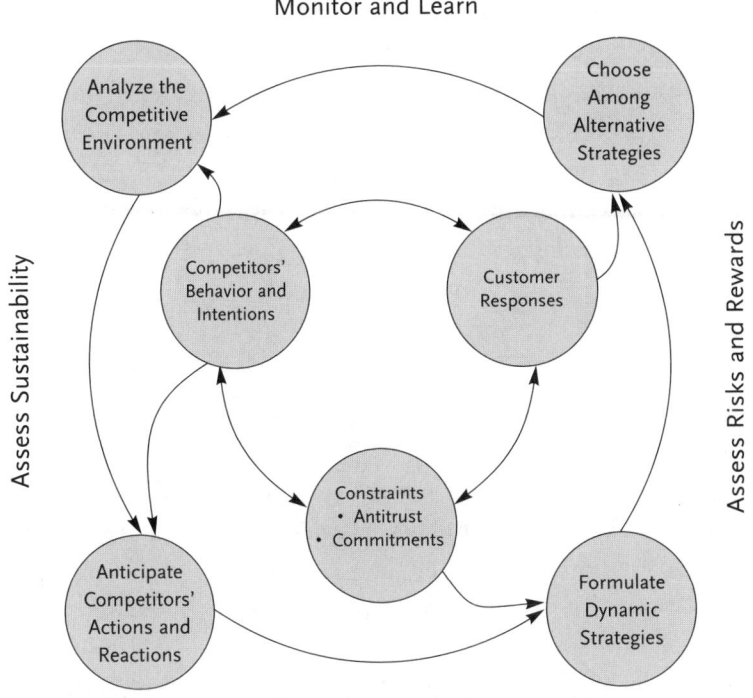

*Source:* G. S. Day and D. J. Reibstein, copyright © 1997. This material is used by permission of John Wiley & Sons, Inc.

4. *Choose among alternative strategies.* Analyze the long-term impact of alternative potential strategies and select one to implement, evaluate possible consequences over multiple periods of competition using simulation or some other approach, and reformulate and revise strategies for the future as appropriate.

Of particular interest in the research of Day and Reibstein (1997) is the detailed description of the alternatives available for dealing with the dynamic nature of competitive strategy, including moves and counter moves, as the war for market position and share play out. Day and Reibstein argue that reacting to competitors' moves can and should be more diverse than merely a variation on the type of competitive move made itself (see Figure 9.2). Also, sometimes the best move is a strong offense and preemption can be an excellent strategy (see Figures 9.3 and 9.4). Finally, they suggest that competition can be viewed as similar to a chess game. In chess, most players can only think a few moves ahead while masters can plan many moves ahead and analyze many different combinations. Competitive strategy should be viewed as analogous to chess, with the most successful players able to excel in the dynamic nature of the game and anticipate and set up well for the inevitable "end game."

Taking the dynamic and increasingly unbounded nature of competitive strategy one step further, Hamel and Prahalad (1994) argue that much of competitive strategy today is being played out in the wrong competitive space. Many companies are still trying to compete (both overall and for the products they offer) by becoming more operationally efficient or by achieving higher quality within the product or market domain in which they operate. The real challenge for the progressive organization is to be different by "fundamentally reconceiving itself, . . . regenerating its core strategies, and . . . reinventing its industry" (Hamel and Prahalad 1994) (see Figure 9.5). Of these new industry leaders, Hamel and Prahalad's research suggests:

> We had to conclude that some management teams were simply more "foresightful" than others. Some were capable of imagining products, services, and entire industries that did not yet exist and then giving them birth. These managers seemed to spend less time worrying about how to position the firm in existing "competitive space" and more time creating fundamentally new competitive space. Other companies, the laggards, were more interested in protecting the past than in creating the future. They took the industry structure as a given, seldom challenging the prevailing conventions.

## Figure 9.2: Decision Model for Determining Response to a New Entrant

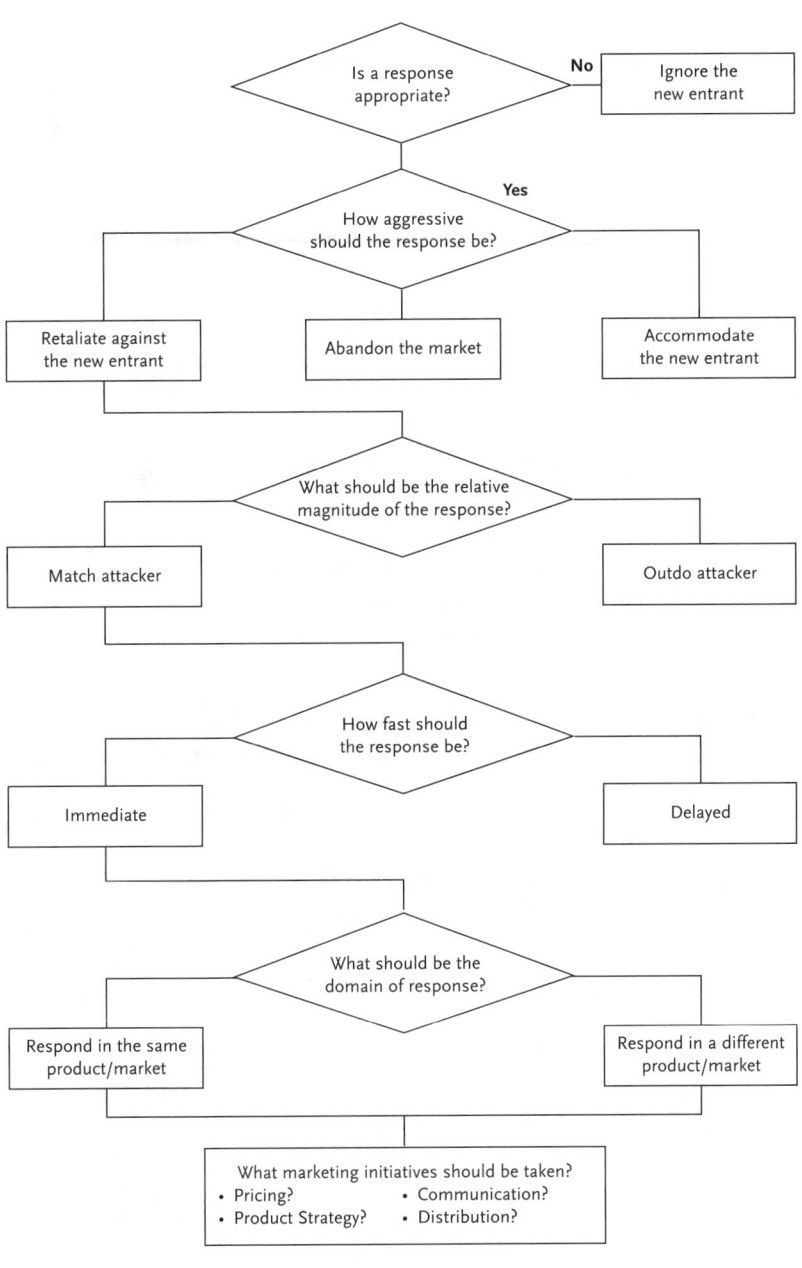

*Source:* G. S. Day and D. J. Reibstein, copyright © 1997. This material is used by permission of John Wiley & Sons, Inc.

*The Future of Healthcare Competitive Strategy*     227

## Figure 9.3: Planning for Preemption

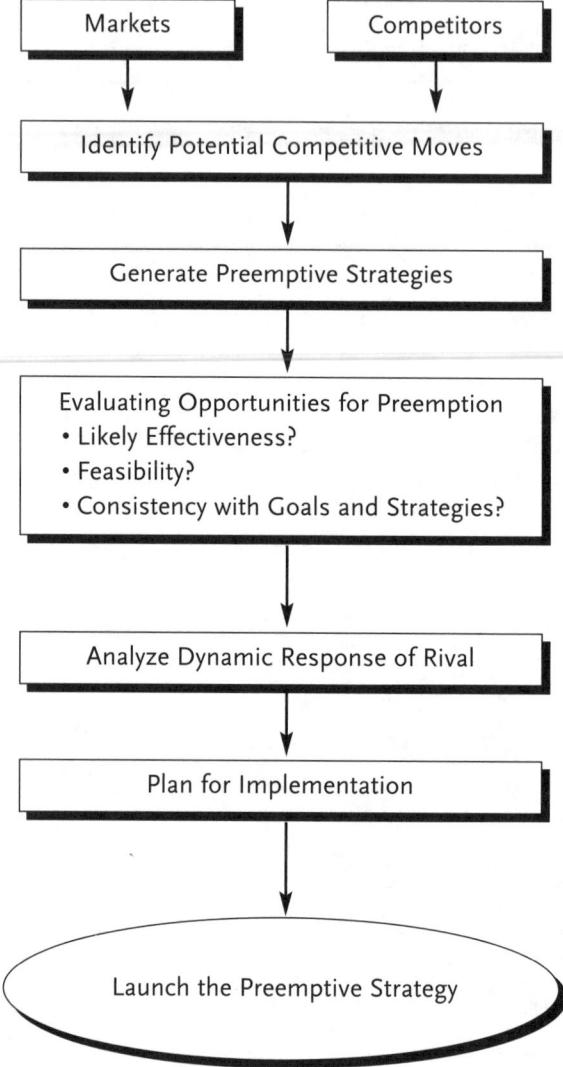

## Figure 9.4: An Illustrative, Preemptive, Option-Generation Grid

The Future of Healthcare Competitive Strategy

**Market Segments**

- Our loyal customers
- Our vulnerable customers
- Our former customers
- Prospects

**Timing**

- Immediately
- Near future
- Few months
- A year or more

**Geographic Scope**

- U.S.
- Selected regions, U.S.
- Selected regions of the world
- Global
- The competitor's home
- Country

**Positioning**

- Premium
- Cost savings
- Quality
- Value added

**Promotion**

- Frequent buyer programs

**Preannouncement**

- No preannouncement
- Preannouncement of new product entry
- Preannouncement of price changes

**Product and Service Offerings**

- Add new services
- Expand the product line
- Introduce a new generation product

**Pricing**

- Long-term contract
- Bundled
- Discount
- Change pricing formula

**Distribution/Logistics**

- Exclusive arrangements
- Loading the channel
- Strategic alliance (M&A)

**Advertising/Communication**

- Endorsements by clients
- "Capture a positioning"
- Exclusive media

**Sources of Supply/Production**

- Secure critical sources
- Vertical integration with key suppliers

**Legal Action**

- Patent infringement
- Trademark
- Deceptive advertising

**Misinformation**

- Send misleading signals

**Key Leverage**

- "Capture the client"
- Tie up distribution
- Distract competition in its key country

*Source:* G. S. Day and D. J. Reibstein, copyright © 1997. This material is used by permission of John Wiley & Sons, Inc.

**Figure 9.5: The Quest for Competitiveness**

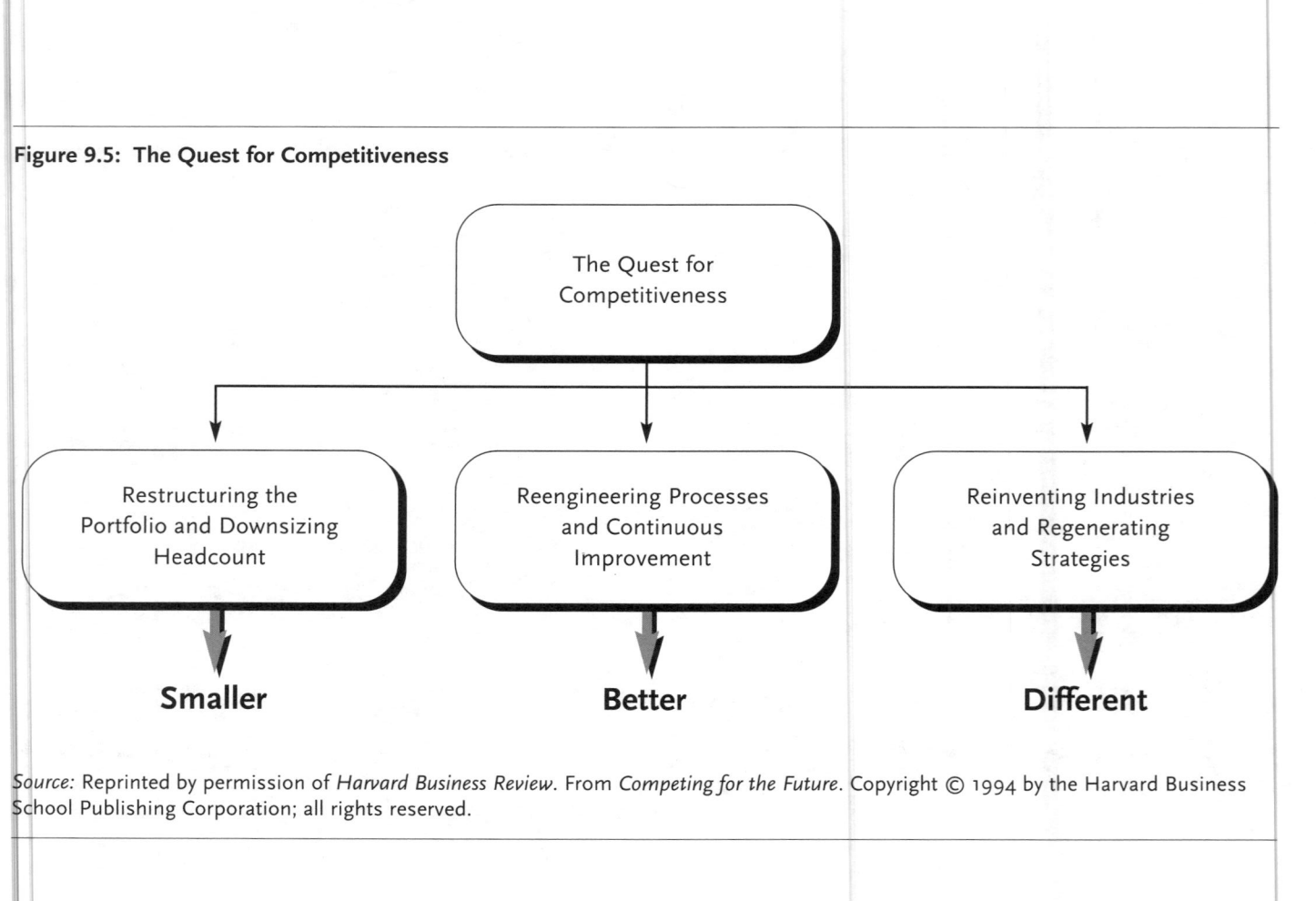

Those more visionary management teams are composed of a high proportion of challengers, innovators, and imaginators. According to Hamel and Prahalad (1994), "They discover the new solutions because they are willing to look far beyond the old" (see Figure 9.6). "The new solutions emerge not because the challengers are incrementally more efficient than the incumbents, but because they are substantially more unorthodox." These visionary management teams are able to (Hamel and Prahalad 1994):

(1) change in some fundamental way the rules of engagment in a long-standing industry (as Charles Schwab did in the brokerage and mutual fund businesses), (2) redraw the boundaries between industries (as Time Warner, Electronic Arts, and other companies are attempting to do in the field of "edutainment"), and/or (3) create entirely new industries (as Apple did in personal computers). A capacity to invent new industries and reinvent old ones is a prerequisite for getting to the future first and a precondition for staying out in front.

Of particular relevance to existing healthcare organizations, Hamel and Prahalad (1994) note that:

Too many managers charged with the task of managing organizational transformation forget to ask, "Transform to what?" The point is that the organizational transformation agenda must be driven by a point of view about the industry transformation agenda: How do we want this industry to be shaped in five or ten years? What must we do to ensure that the industry evolves in a way that is maximally advantageous for us? What skills and capabilities must we begin building now if we are to occupy the industry high ground in the future? And how should we organize for opportunities that may not fit neatly within the boundaries of current business units and divisions? A point of view about the desired trajectory for industry transformation enables a company to create a proactive agenda for organizational transformation.

**Figure 9.6: Why Do Great Companies Fail?**

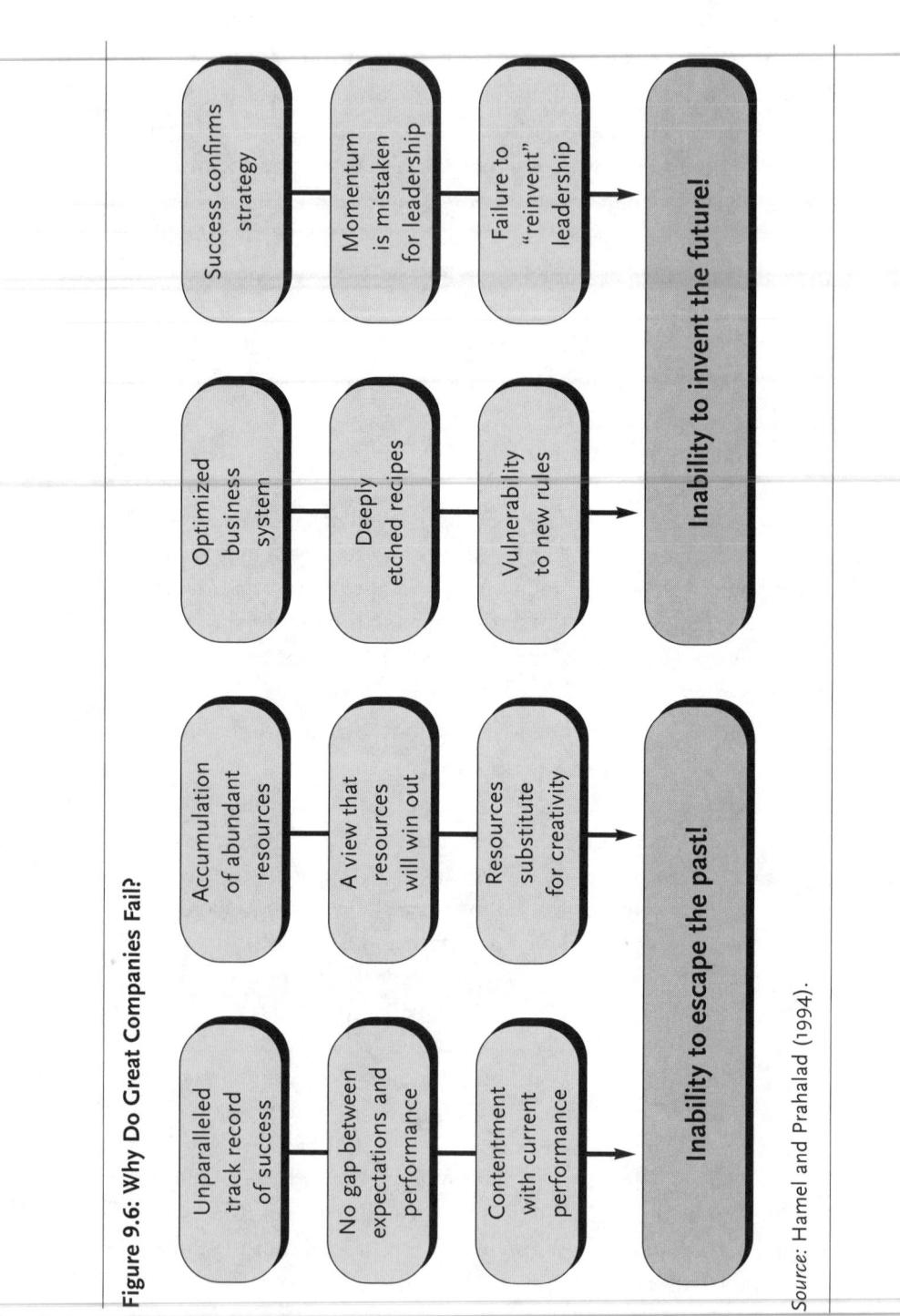

*Source:* Hamel and Prahalad (1994).

Finally, the authors suggest that their new view of competitive strategy requires four elements for a company to successfully implement it (Hamel and Prahalad 1994):

(1) an understanding of how competition for the future is different; (2) a process for finding and gaining insight into tomorrow's opportunities; (3) an ability to energize the company top-to-bottom for what may be a long and arduous journey toward the future; and (4) the capacity to outrun competitors and get to the future first, without taking undue risks.

In summary, Hamel and Prahalad's point of view is that "[c]ompetition for the future is competition to create and dominate emerging opportunities—to stake out new competitive space" (Hamel and Prahalad 1994) (see Figure 9.7).

## COMPETING ON THE EDGE

Brown and Eisenhardt (1998) take Hamel and Prahalad's thesis one step further in their recent book that focuses on rapidly and unpredictably changing industries. They recommend that these situations demand a strategy they label "competing on the edge," which is defined as being "the creation of a relentless flow of competitive advantage [driven by] the ability to change."

It has five key building blocks: improvisation, coadaptation, regeneration, experimentation, and time pacing. At its heart, competing on the edge meets the strategic challenge of change by constantly reshaping competitive advantage even as the marketplace unpredictably and rapidly shifts. The goal is reinvention through a relentless flow of competitive advantages. In terms of strategy, competing on the edge ties "Where do you want to go?" intimately to "How are you going to get there?" The result is an unpredictable, uncontrollable, and even inefficient strategy that nonetheless . . . works.

**Figure 9.7: The New Strategy Paradigm**

| NOT ONLY | BUT ALSO |
|---|---|

*The Competitive Challenge*

| | |
|---|---|
| Reengineering processes | Regenerating strategies |
| Organizational transformation | Industry transformation |
| Competing for market share | Competing for opportunity share |

*Finding the Future*

| | |
|---|---|
| Strategy as learning | Strategy as forgetting |
| Strategy as positioning | Strategy as foresight |
| Strategic plans | Strategic architecture |

*Mobilizing for the Future*

| | |
|---|---|
| Strategy as fit | Strategy as stretch |
| Strategy as resource allocation | Strategy as resource accumulation and leverage |

*Getting to the Future First*

| | |
|---|---|
| Competing within an existing industry structure | Competing to shape future industry structure |
| Competing for product leadership | Competing for core competence leadership |
| Competing as a single entity | Competing as a coalition |
| Maximizing the ratio of new product "hits" | Maximizing the rate of new market learning |
| Minimizing time-to-market | Minimizing time to global preemption |

*Source:* Hamel and Prahalad (1994).

Like Hamel and Prahalad, Brown and Eisenhardt (1998) preach the importance of shaping the future industry and market, not just reacting to events as they occur (see Figure 9.8). They, too, cite numerous examples of firms that altered the rules of the game and are pacesetters in their industry.

## Figure 9.8: Managing the Strategic Challenge of Change

| Levels of Change | Events | Strategy |
|---|---|---|
| **Leading** | • Create new technologies and products<br>• Launch new markets<br>• Raise industry standards<br>• Redefine customer expectations<br>• Increase pace of industry product cycles | • Force other firms to follow |
| **Anticipating** | • Globalization of markets<br>• Creation of new customer segments<br>• Emergence of conflicting technologies | • Line up resources (e.g., venture partners, cross-cultural employees, currency trading skills) early<br>• Develop corresponding marketing channels<br>• Create technical options |
| **Reacting** | • Competitor's product moves<br>• New government policies<br>• Unexpected customer demands | • Release better products<br>• Create services that exploit change<br>• Repackage existing products |

*Source:* Brown and Eisenhardt (1998).

Their premise is that many contemporary industries are faced with high-velocity unpredictable change. The old, static models of competitive strategy that assume clear industry boundaries, known competitors, and an ability to forecast the future are outmoded in this environment. Even the recent dynamic models, while more sensitive to the pace of change that is occurring, are nonetheless incomplete and only provide temporary, short-term advantage at best (see Figure 9.9).

Competing on the edge concurrently combines the two parts of strategy—Where do you want to go? and How do you get there?—in an approach that effectively addresses the reality of a fast and ever-changing environment (see Figure 9.10). This approach results in what Brown and Eisenhardt (1998) term a "semicoherent direction" that defines where the organization is going and a set of behaviors (akin to competitive strategies) that allow the organization to get where it is going. These behaviors are both structured and unstructured ("edge of chaos"), recognize the past and envision potential futures ("edge of time") and develop an internal rhythm that creates the momentum for change ("time pacing"). Implementing this type of strategy allows the organization faced with the extreme market conditions described above to change continuously and lead its industry into the future.

## CONCLUSION

While healthcare delivery may not be challenged yet by the high-velocity changes occurring in many high-technology industries, the rate of change is increasingly rapid and often unpredictable. Healthcare organizations have experienced major environmental change in recent years as a result of federal legislation and regulations, pharmaceutical and technological breakthroughs, the Internet, and other forces. These types of change will increasingly become the norm, creating a much more dynamic and rapidly shifting market.

**Figure 9.9: Models of Strategy**

| | Five Forces | Core Competence | Game Theory | Competing on the Edge |
|---|---|---|---|---|
| ASSUMPTIONS | Stable industry structure | Firm as bundle of competences | Industry viewed as dynamic oligopoly | Industry in rapid, unpredictable change |
| GOAL | Defensible position | Sustainable advantage | Temporary advantage | Continuous flow of advantages |
| PERFORMANCE DRIVER | Industry structure | Unique firm competences | Right moves | Ability to change |
| STRATEGY | Pick an industry, pick a strategic position, fit the organization | Create a vision, build and exploit competences to realize vision | Make the "right" competitive and collaborative moves | Gain the "edges," time pace, shape semicoherent strategic direction |
| SUCCESS | Profits | Long-term dominance | Short-term win | Continual reinvention |

*Source:* Brown and Eisenhardt (1998).

**Figure 9.10: Competing on the Edge**

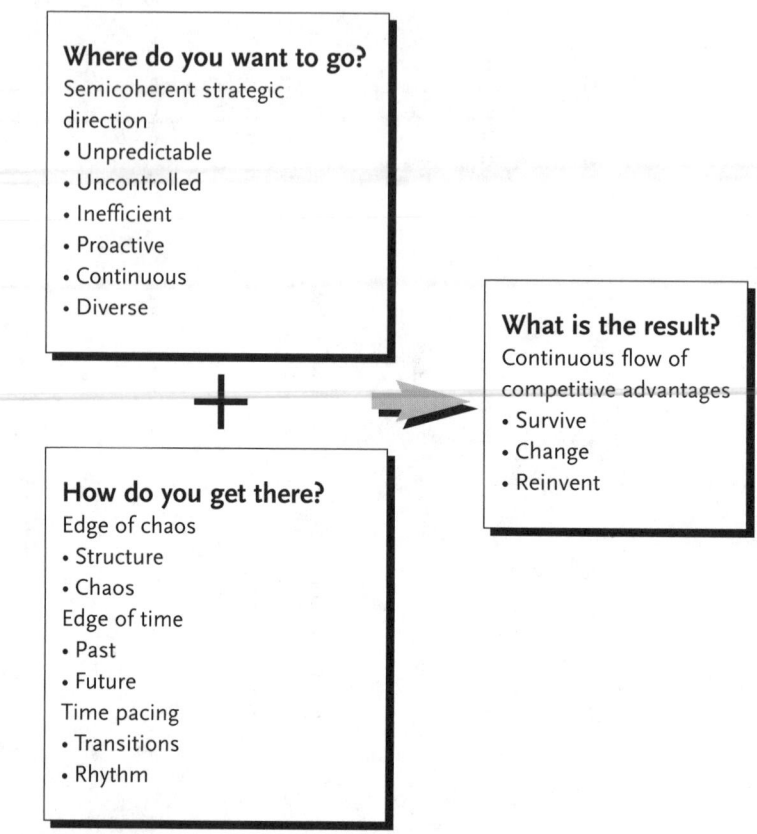

**Where do you want to go?**
Semicoherent strategic direction
• Unpredictable
• Uncontrolled
• Inefficient
• Proactive
• Continuous
• Diverse

**How do you get there?**
Edge of chaos
• Structure
• Chaos
Edge of time
• Past
• Future
Time pacing
• Transitions
• Rhythm

**What is the result?**
Continuous flow of competitive advantages
• Survive
• Change
• Reinvent

As a result of recent changes, industry boundaries are being redrawn and new competitors emerging, seemingly out of nowhere. Examples include the rise of alternative and complementary medicine, assisted-living facilities, heart hospitals, and other new segments. At the same time, new competitors appear on the scene and sometimes vanish, such as MedCath (still here) and PhyCor (now gone). Among not-for-profits, recent years have seen the pursuit of international patient business and Internet strategies that erode traditional geographic boundaries.

## REFERENCES

Burns, L. R. 2000. "Competitive Strategy." Unpublished manuscript, February, pp. 15–16.

Brown, S. L. and K. M. Eisenhardt. 1998. *Competing on the Edge.* Boston: Harvard Business School Press.

Day, G. S., and D. J. Reibstein (Eds.). 1997. *Wharton on Dynamic Competitive Strategy.* New York: John Wiley.

Hamel, G., and C. K. Prahalad. 1994. *Competing for the Future.* Cambridge, MA: Harvard Business School Press.

Shortell, S. M., E. M. Morrison, and B. Friedman. 1990. *Strategic Choices for America's Hospitals: Managing Change in Turbulent Times.* San Francisco: Jossey-Bass.

# CHAPTER 10

# Ten Lessons for Healthcare Competitive Strategy in the Twenty-first Century

## INTRODUCTION

COMPETITIVE STRATEGY FOR healthcare organizations will clearly not be a simple undertaking in the twenty-first century. But all of the complex activities and considerations discussed throughout this book can be synthesized into ten lessons presented in this chapter that serve as the framework for taking current healthcare competitive strategy to new levels.

## LESSON 1: COMMIT TO COMPETING

The healthcare market has been and will continue to be a competitive one. All organizations are competing to greater or lesser degrees, and every product each organization offers operates in a competitive market. Even in somewhat isolated areas competition exists. Geographic boundaries and barriers provide less protection every day as information and communication advances continue to shrink the world. Although some would like to ignore or deny that healthcare organizations operate in a fiercely competitive market, it is a fact of life. And being a not-for-profit organization provides no safe harbor or immunity from the realities of the marketplace.

A key part of lesson 1 is resolving to be a serious competitor. As this book describes, being a serious competitor means critically evaluating the organization in its entirety and each major product or service it offers. It means looking outside the organization, both at current and potential future competitors and at the environment in which the organization operates today and in the future. To position healthcare organizations successfully for the future involves critical and careful examination of internal and external situations and a willingness to adapt, at a minimum, to meet foreseeable future needs. In fact, as the latest and most advanced research on competitive strategy points out, change should be embraced as a way of life in the organization.

These statements may sound contrived or trivial, but they represent a truly fundamental shift for the typical not-for-profit healthcare organization. Without this fundamental change in perspective, all the tools and approaches described in this book will not be particularly useful.

## LESSON 2: AVOID "COPYCAT" STRATEGIES

The herd mentality in healthcare is strong, and recent history is replete with examples of the majority of organizations adopting a certain competitive model to ensure success. In the 1980s diversification was guaranteed to protect against the likelihood of eventual below-cost inpatient reimbursement. In the 1990s the success model was integrated delivery designed to create large organizations to dominate the market and offer one-stop shopping to the consumer and guarantee that managed care contracts would be gained and managed effectively. It is not clear what the next "sure fire" success strategy of the first decade of the twenty-first century will be; however, if the past is any guide, whatever it is will be no guarantee of success.

As the business literature and examples in preceding chapters demonstrate no one model or approach works in every situation for every organization. There are some tried and true models and approaches, but the ability to carry out any of them successfully is very much a function of the particular situation facing an organization and the market in which it operates. And the latest research suggests even those models and approaches may no longer be valid in today's more dynamic marketplace.

At best, copycat strategies should be viewed by senior leadership of an organization with suspicion if not rejected outright. The main value of copycat strategies is in competitor analysis— if some of your organization's competitors appear to be employing a particular type of common strategy, it is easier to discern what they are doing and how to respond to it effectively in a more creative and customized manner.

## LESSON 3: REALIZE SUCCESS CANNOT BE FOUND IN A COOKBOOK

Lesson 3 is a derivative of the copycat strategy principle. Some readers may have picked up this book hoping to find a competitive strategy cookbook. What the reader found instead was a number of well-tested recipes, but little guarantee of success should you try to employ them.

It is clear that healthcare has evolved over an approximately 20-year period from a situation where supply had trouble keeping up with demand and suppliers (i.e., provider organizations) operated in a highly protected environment to a situation with almost classic competitive characteristics: supply of almost every product or service exceeds demand, regulation is much less limiting, and entry and exit of providers into and from the market is fairly fluid.

In the beginning of this era, reasonably simple and simplistic competitive strategies could achieve great success and occasionally did. By the midpoint of this transition period, competitive strategies required for success were already somewhat complex and many established providers began to falter as a result of weak strategy.

Within the past few years, few healthcare organizations have escaped a significant downturn and the rate of failure has become alarmingly high; although reimbursement is certainly a major factor in the industrywide downturn, poorly conceived competitive strategy is also a culprit with healthcare organizations falling prey to copycat and cookbook approaches.

Although the preceding chapters provide some standard approaches to competitive analysis and competitive strategy, these can hardly be reduced to a formulaic approach. Success will come from doing the right things with rigor and foresight and from a great deal of ongoing and increasingly creative, hard work.

## LESSON 4: BUILD GOOD STRATEGY WITH GOOD INTELLIGENCE

The fundamental building block for competitive strategy is competitor and market intelligence. It is not surprising, therefore, that intelligence is deficient and a weak link in most healthcare organizations' competitive arsenal.

For too long, healthcare organizations have claimed that lack of available data and information renders thoughtful strategy and planning impossible. Instead of hiding behind the excuse of data availability and continuing to be largely inward looking (where data do exist), efforts need to be directed toward developing much more sophisticated approaches to data gathering as described in chapter 8. Healthcare organizations that have dedicated resources to more thorough and penetrating information gathering have been rewarded for their efforts. Rather than finding that there is a dearth of competitor and market information, the opposite in fact is discovered and the challenge is to turn the wealth of data discovered into useful information.

In these efforts, value in both primary and secondary data gathering is gained. Although much can be learned from the data already in the public or semipublic domain, targeted primary research can fill critical holes in competitor and market intelligence.

For-profit organizations operating in healthcare have used intelligence gathering with great success, and this alone has provided them with a major competitive advantage over not-for-profits. A critical review of publicly available information such as federal Securities and Exchange Commission filings, state reports and required filings, annual reports, and web sites will illustrate how for-profit healthcare organizations have used information to their advantage.

## LESSON 5: BUILD STRONG STRATEGY WITH ANALYSIS

Without comprehensive, in-depth information, the next step to developing contemporary competitive strategy, competitor, and market analyses, is not possible. Competitor intelligence provides the raw material for and inputs to analysis, turning often basic data into valuable information and insights.

The preceding two chapters have described and discussed various methods for competitor and market analysis as well as what, in general, we should be able to learn from this effort. This analysis, although historically primarily directed at the operations and activities of each existing competitor, also needs to be concerned with the potential opportunities in the market that may lead to future competitors as well as with a thorough understanding of market conditions and dynamics. Competitor and market analysis needs to address the past and present, but also the future.

For-profits in healthcare also illustrate the potential advantages to be reaped from solid competitor and market analysis. A review of publicly available information, especially the 10-K reports filed annually with the Securities and Exchange Commission, provides great insight into how for-profits have used this intelligence to dissect competitors' behaviors and plans to establish market assumptions, forecasts, and the resulting strategy that is derived from this analysis.

Competitor and market analysis is an essential second step to building strong strategy. It begins to move the organization from looking at the past to visualizing and creating the future and is an important transition to subsequent competitive strategy steps.

## LESSON 6: ENVISION THE FUTURE

If we have learned nothing else from history, we know it is hard to envision the future. Who would have predicted the fall of communism in the late 1980s and early 1990s and the subsequent collapse of the Soviet Union? Who would have predicted the long bull market in stocks in the 1990s or the subsequent sharp downturn? Nearly everyone thought managed care would sweep the country and that by the year 2000 essentially all Americans would be enrolled in a managed care plan, yet obviously nothing close to this phenomenon occurred. Despite these and many other examples of unpredictable future outcomes, no element of competitive strategy is as important as thinking about the future.

A number of important concepts emerge from the latest research on this subject. Members of management teams need to spend more time envisioning the future individually and collectively. Since the future is so unpredictable, multiple scenarios of future characteristics and states should be developed. Whatever strategies and plans are ultimately pursued, given the uncertainty about the future, alternatives and contingencies need to be considered, too.

Because the competitive strategy is intended to be employed in the future, extensive and critical thinking about the future and the applicability of any proposed strategy to potential future conditions and circumstances is essential. Time spent envisioning the future will increase the likelihood that any strategies developed will be appropriate to the future state and therefore have a reasonable chance for success.

## LESSON 7: DEVELOP A VISION

Part of envisioning the future is creating a picture of what the organization and its key subcomponent products and services might look like in the future. The vision should be a desired future state and represent an achievable state of being, but one that is also a stretch from its current position. The vision can serve as a beacon in the distance, while strategy in general and competitive strategy in particular helps to navigate the organization and its key components toward that hazy and distant image.

Some of the examples cited in previous chapters speak to the importance of having a vision. In certain instances, companies have invented entirely new industries (e.g., Apple and personal computers) to address a very different sense of the future and the opportunity for a totally new way of doing business or carrying out many personal tasks. In others, companies and their key products and services have been largely or totally redesigned (e.g., consumer banking through ATMs and the Internet) to address vastly different future market conditions and needs. Even in those instances where cataclysmic change did not occur (e.g., Marriott and the hospitality industry), vision was helpful in transforming a company and its key subcomponents into a more successful competitor.

Having a vision is an essential part of designing effective competitor strategy. If leadership does not know where its organization is headed, it is hard to design an effective strategy to take the company there. While some of the latest research on business strategy indicates that the vision may be somewhat more vague and less distinct than is traditionally believed to be appropriate, it nonetheless reinforces the concept of establishing as clear a vision as possible to guide effective strategy development.

## LESSON 8: ADDRESS THE ACCELERATING PACE OF CHANGE

One of the underlying themes of the research on competitive strategy, which begins in the 1970s and covers the last three decades of the twentieth century, is the United States' and worldwide transition from a relatively stable business environment into a much more dynamic, global, and ever-changing one. This theme of the accelerating pace of change is at the heart of the development of each generation of new approaches to competitive strategy, from the fairly simple analytical framework of Boston Consulting Group and others in the 1970s to Porter's five forces and three basic competitive strategy models of the 1980s, to the next generation of Porter's and others' more dynamic models in the 1990s, to the latest generation as represented by Brown and Eisenhardt in the late 1990s.

Whereas the rate of change in the healthcare environment appears to lag behind the general business community due to greater regulation and a number of other factors, the pace of change in healthcare continues to accelerate and each new month and year brings a new peak. Thus, the frameworks proposed to deal with healthcare competitive strategy, as typified by the four archetypes of Miles and Snow in the late 1970s and Shortell and others in the late 1980s and early 1990s are too static and basic to deal with the realities of the early twenty-first century.

A fundamental premise in any approach to competitive strategy in healthcare today needs to be that change is occurring at a faster rate. Competitive strategy needs to recognize this inevitability explicitly and be complex, dynamic, and fluid enough to address this continually shifting marketplace. For most organizations, incorporating the elements of the approaches recommended in the business writings of the 1990s will be sufficient for now to put them in the first rank of healthcare organizations in this area; but the next generation of approaches needs to be monitored and elements implemented as the pace of change accelerates over the next five to ten years.

## LESSON 9: APPLY ADVANCED COMPETITIVE STRATEGY

Four main concepts dominate the recommendations for competitive strategy approaches in the business literature of the 1990s: sustainability, continuity, dynamism, and reinvention.

Gaining competitive advantage is of little value if the advantage is only temporary and not sustainable. Experts in the field firmly reject the trends in the general business community of the late 1980s and early 1990s (and prevalent in healthcare shortly thereafter) to restructure and reengineer the organization to success. Although true cost leadership as advocated by Porter can provide sustainable competitive advantage in some industries even today, it is generally agreed that little of what occurred outside of healthcare (or within) in the last part of the twentieth century to create operational efficiencies constituted sustainable advantage. Only by creating formidable barriers to imitation and by implementing strategies that are truly different from those of the competitors can sustainable competitive advantage be achieved.

The dynamic nature of competitive strategy and a continuous process of strategy reevaluation and regeneration go hand in hand. Even sustainable advantages can only be kept up for some period before advantages may erode or markets may change significantly. Given the increasing pace of change and the rising degree of competition, an ongoing process to continually evaluate market changes and the moves of competitors and to counter them is essential to continued success.

Finally, the latest research emphasizes the increasingly critical importance of a focus on the future and the potential for reinvention or significant restructuring of whole industries and markets. As market boundaries vanish or are redrawn and the markets themselves redefined, the notion of competitive strategy itself becomes increasingly unbounded. Thus, the old rules and approaches, which assumed the relative stability of markets, often are no longer valid.

## LESSON 10: APPLY THE NEW COMPETITIVE STRATEGY

Although the healthcare industry is probably not ready yet for the new competitive strategy, this era is approaching rapidly. Three factors auger an era of unprecedented change for healthcare organizations:

1. The Internet has resulted in an unimaginable amount of medical information available to the public and promises even greater consumer awareness and choice about healthcare options.
2. E-commerce implementation, only in its nascent stage in healthcare, has the potential to completely redefine and redraw markets.
3. Even more significant is the potential of genomics to eradicate major disease categories and, through early detection of at-risk populations, eliminate many common methods of healthcare diagnosis and treatment; entirely new forms of disease management and care may be invented at a rapid and disruptive rate and replace today's common approaches.

## CONCLUSION

These and other developments will render today's approaches to competitive strategy obsolete and create conditions that are ripe for the next generation of approaches as represented by the "competing on the edge" framework described at the end of chapter 9 or other even more groundbreaking methodologies. A new future, more change, and untraditional approaches to competitive strategy are the only certainties of the next generation of developments in the healthcare industry.

# Index

and Health System, 183–84; Maytag Corporation, 171–72; mistakes, 168–69; Nordstrom, 173–74; potential, 164; product, 158, 170–71, 194–99; quality, 158, 171–73, 178–84; representative sources, 163; research implications, 168–70; Salick Health Care, 192–93; service, 158, 173–75, 184–94; Sony Corporation, 172–73; sources, 168; supply side, 165–67; switching costs, 168; Texas Heart Institute, 197–99; 3M, 171

Digital telecommunications, 115–16

Direct Community Investment Fund, 70–71

Directional strategies, 14

Disease management model, 100

Diseconomies of scale, 68

Disney Channel, 36

Disney Internet Group, 35–36, 40

Disneyland, 37–38

Diversification: appropriateness, 17; Berkshire Hathaway Inc., 85–89; competitive advantage, 84–85; definition, 14, 81–82; financial performance and, 13; General Electric, 89–92; Joslin Diabetes Center, Inc., 99–102; rationale, 82; reasons for, 82–84, 242; selective, 221; UniHealth America, 96–99

Diversity, 209

Divestiture, 18, 19

Divisional strategy, 17, 19

Dogs, 5–6

DRG. See Diagnosis-related group

Duncan, W. J.: cost strategy, 146; differentiation strategy, 175–76; diversification, 93; growth framework, 14–19, 23

Dynamics, 249

Eastaugh, S. R., 95

E-commerce, 250

Economies of learning, 135

Economies of operation, 29, 30

Economies of scale, 68, 110, 135

Edison Electric Light Company, 89

Edsel B. Ford Institute for Medical Research, 44

Efficiency, 41

Eisenhardt, K. M., 233–36

Eisner, Michael, 39, 40

Elliott P. Joslin Research Laboratory, 100

Enhancement, 19

Entry barriers, 159

ESPN International, 36

Excess capacity, 209

Excessive differentiation, 169

Excess supply, 2

Exit barriers, 209

Expansion strategy, 14, 16–17

Faulkner, D., 3, 210–11

FedEx Corporation, 174–75

Ferrari, Bernard, 60

Financial performance: differentiation strategy, 177; diversification and, 82, 95; indicators, 12–13

Financial services, 64–66

Finnish Cable Works, 115

Finnish Rubberworks, 115

Finova Group, 88

Floyd, William, 74

Focused competition, 108–10

Focus strategy, 4

Friedman, B.: competitive advantage, 221–22; differentiation strategy, 177; diversification, 95–96

Gannett, Frank, 119

Gannett Company, Inc., 118–21

GDP. See Gross domestic product

GE. See General Electric

GEICO, 89

General Electric (GE), 7, 8, 89–92

General Re, 87, 88–89

Generic strategies, 4

Genomics, 250

Gerimed, 123

Ginter, P. M.: cost strategy, 146; differentiation strategy, 175–76; diversification, 93; growth framework, 14–19, 23

Grant, Robert: competitor analysis, 210, 211–15; cost drivers, 135, 137; cost strategy, 134; differentiation strategy, 157, 162, 167; diversification, 84–85; industry analysis, 208, 210

# About the Author

Alan M. Zuckerman, FACHE, FAAHC, is a founding partner and director of Health Strategies & Solutions, Inc., a leading national healthcare consulting firm. Mr. Zuckerman has been a management consultant for 30 years, working exclusively for healthcare providers across the United States.

During his career, Mr. Zuckerman's consulting work has focused on strategic planning; this book is an outgrowth of his experience with hundreds of diverse healthcare organizations. Among his strategic planning clients have been large and small community hospitals, academic medical centers, single and multispecialty physician groups, nursing homes, retirement centers, hospices, home care agencies, and psychiatric and rehabilitation specialty centers. In recent years, he has been involved in the development of increasingly sophisticated competitive strategies for leading hospitals, health systems, and academic medical centers.

Mr. Zuckerman is widely published and a frequent speaker at national healthcare conferences. His book *Healthcare Strategic Planning: Approaches for the 21st Century* won the 1999 American

College of Healthcare Executives' James A. Hamilton book-of-the-year award. Mr. Zuckerman is a fellow of the American College of Healthcare Executives and of the American Association of Healthcare Consultants and a member of the Society for Healthcare Strategy and Market Development.